Dr. Sollars and Jamie Sharpe deliv⟨ ⟩ approach to better understand ou⟨ ⟩ relates to the world around us. The⟨ ⟩ ...⟨ ⟩ ...actionable steps and is easily guided through a process of growth that will empower all readers toward living a more full and authentic life.

Ryan G. Beale, MA
CEO/Founder of Therapy.Live

I am delighted with your beautiful synthesis of depth psychology and metaphysical perspectives. You provide basic and clearly stated concepts along with useful and relatable examples. This workbook provides the fundamentals of inner work. An invaluable tool for those already engaged with in depth therapy and those who may embark on their own self-therapy.

I salute your careful, meticulous and comprehensive cartography of the terrain of the inner psyche, as well as the exercises and meditations that bridge the esoteric and the practical.

Brian O'Donnell, PhD
Psychotherapist in private practice, Ann Arbor, MI
Instructor at Pathwork

The *Love Outraged Workbook* offers readers an experiential way to interact with concepts and processes outlined in the previously published *Love Outraged and the Liberation of the Core Self*. With deceptively simple exercises, Sollars invites readers to break the Promethean chains of self-alienation by identifying and befriending the thoughts, feelings and defenses that contribute to estrangement from the core self. Accessible to clinicians and laypeople alike, *The Love Outraged Workbook* is more than a workbook; it is a map of the human condition, a user friendly and accessible path home to the deepest center of being.

Rev. Dr. Betz King
Psychologist, Western Mystery Tradition Priestess, Reiki Master

The Love Outraged Workbook

by
Franklin Sollars
&
Jamie Sharpe

University
PROFESSORS PRESS

Colorado Springs, CO
www.universityprofessorspress.com

The Love Outraged Workbook
By Franklin Sollars & Jamie Sharpe

First published in 2020, University Professors Press

ISBN: 978-1-939686-52-7

University Professors Press
Colorado Springs, CO
http://www.universityprofessorspress.com

Cover Photo by Franklin Sollars
Cover Design by Laura Ross, 2019

Table of Contents

Acknowledgments

Enormous thanks to my wife, Shelley, for her support and encouragement of my writing. I would also like to thank some of my teachers. Eva Pierrakos and her lectures have always been a guiding light in my life. Much of my Love Outraged series is underpinned by the mystical inspiration of her work. Mike Eigen, John Saly, Henry Krystal, Barnaby Barratt, Berta McKay, Bill Wahlberg, and Murry Meisels were all mentors and helpers that have had significant influence on my writing. Thanks to Jamie Sharpe for her collaboration on this workbook; her work has helped make the difficult concepts in the book more accessible.

~ Franklin Sollars

First and foremost, I am eternally grateful to my family. To my parents for laying the foundation for who I am today and supporting me incessantly throughout my life. To my brothers for emboldening me from the very beginning and continuing to do so as we grow older. To my grandma for instilling in me the importance of love and laughter.

I am especially thankful to my significant other for being patient as I learn more about who I am and for being willing to grow with me. To my extended family and closest friends for encouraging me to pursue my professional aspirations, despite each new endeavor taking away from time I could be spending with you.

Finally, I would also like to give a special thanks to Dr. Sollars for inviting me to collaborate with him to create this work and be a part of this journey.

~ Jamie Sharpe

Foreword

These days, many people seem to be in desperate pursuit of "happiness." Clients often come into our offices lamenting that they "just want to be happy." In his previous book, *Love Outraged*, psychologist, professor, and author Franklin Sollars, Ph.D., guided us on an exploration of how our own particular happiness can be found not externally, but in an embodied self who realizes its potential through accessing what Sollars calls the "core self." Only by understanding the fullness of the "core self" can we manifest our most creative creation, which is a rich, lush, sacred, and deeply appreciated life.

How wonderful then, that *Love Outraged* and its powerful blueprint for self-actualization has a new compendium exercise book, *The Love Outraged Workbook*, helping us further integrate the important theories we learned in *Love Outraged* into a daily life that feels refreshed, aerated, and is wholeheartedly embraced by us as we continue to learn and hone "core self" skills and all the healing possibilities therein.

Written by Dr. Sollars, along with doctoral student, Jamie Sharp, this personal growth handbook is a useful supplement to educational materials available to students in psychology, and other mental health professionals, giving them a well-articulated perspective of depth psychology, emotional development, and spiritual understanding, both theoretical and practical. The companion publications of *Love Outraged* and its workbook will become favorite go-to resources, applicable to work in the field of clinical practice.

The Love Outraged Workbook is a wonderful series of meditations geared toward discovery of one's vitally important "core self," and through that discovery, the ability to uncover and disclose "unique gifts" and talents. The workbook clearly describes follow-along exercises to cultivate and bring to life healthy expressions of the "core self." Laid out in an easy to follow organizational style, *The Love Outraged Workbook* is filled with fascinating depth psychology concepts followed by useful prompts and exercises to help readers explore their own depth psychology process, and understand how this humanistic approach to emotional and spiritual growth is a sure way to achieve what most of us are looking for: a full and meaningful life that feels authentic and wholly-lived.

If creating happiness is the aspiration, or helping our clients and patients do so, The *Love Outraged Workbook* additionally helps readers do the hard work of examining the shadows of our human nature, through analysis of seemingly negative forces, such as "fears" and "limited view," as we seek insight into emotionally paralyzing conditions and "blocks" to our innate self-actualizing tendency. The workbook's sections look at such critical life issues as:

- Becoming totally responsible for your life
- Reigniting the "core self"
- Transforming envy, contempt, arrogance, vanity, and perfectionism into healthy self-love
- Using honest self-appraisal as a way to discern "Why am I standing in my own way?"

The Love Outraged Workbook encourages us to glean insight into the inherent loving qualities of the "core self" within all of us, which naturally come forth and organically manifest when we take genuine responsibility for our lives, and fully embody our unique and extraordinary existential journeys. By reading the *Love Outraged Workbook* and using its prompts in both personal and professional applications, we become keenly aware through the book exercises that happiness does indeed become a welcome and ecstatically experienced byproduct of liberating the "core self," and its natural loving energy.

Discovery of the potential for such liberation and living from the "core self" is great news for the client and the therapist, as well as all those whose lives they touch.

~ Donna Rockwell, PsyD

Donna Rockwell, PsyD, is past-president of the Society for Humanistic Psychology, Division 32 of the American Psychological Association, and Adjunct Faculty at Saybrook University in the College of Integrative Medicine and Health Sciences. She was trained by Humanistic Psychology founder Clark Moustakas, Ph.D., in humanistic existential approaches to psychology, play therapy, and qualitative research. Dr. Rockwell specializes in mindfulness in psychotherapy, and the psychology of fame and celebrity mental health.

Introduction

After the publication of *Love Outraged*, it became clear that many of the concepts I discussed in the book, while philosophically accessible to people, were difficult to understand in a way that would allow them to be immediately usable for emotional and spiritual growth. This workbook is an attempt to help the reader grapple with many of these concepts and more easily make use of them for their personal journey or for the therapist or counselor to employ in their help of others.

To be effective, this workbook cannot simply be read. It will require some self-examination and the ability to accept some faults in ourselves that might be felt to be unflattering at times. In the end, the goal of the book is the transformation of our shadow or negative personality elements to help us with emotional and spiritual growth and help liberate us from our fears.

Assisting me with this book was an outstanding psychology graduate student, Ms. Jamie Sharpe. Jamie is working toward the completion of her doctorate in psychology and has a great understanding of the text and a closeness to graduate and undergraduate psychology. She therefore was invaluable in helping make the material more experience-near for people.

In the workbook we offer many examples of experiential work with the concepts. We also offer ways for each reader to work personally with the material by having the reader bring their own issues or tensions to mind, write them down, and then apply the corrective or illuminating challenges that *Love Outraged* offers to assuage their troubles. Hopefully, this will help bring the concepts to life as a reader goes through the text.

We also place parenthetical page references in the workbook to help connect the workbook concepts to the original *Love Outraged* text. This adds a layered richness to the concepts and helps foster a deeper understanding of the material.

Finally, we often use a dialectical approach in explaining the concepts. That is, we talk about the concepts from one side and then the other and back again to help illuminate an understanding. This manner of writing I have often found helpful with difficult material.

Chapter 1
The Core Self

The "Core Self," (LO, pp. 10, 12-13, 19-22, 25, 29, 31-33, 39-40), which can be found in psychoanalytic and psychological literature, has been written about historically, in one form or another, in all the major religions. It is the fountain of love, inspiration and wisdom that lies at the deepest center of our being. It is both who we are individually and a portal that connects us with every other being and the world around us in empathic resonance. We vibrate harmonically as one when the Core is dropped into and embraced.

This Core contains what we experience as a paradox in our everyday consciousness. That is, we are uniquely ourselves as individuals yet identified as one with everything. This Core is sometimes felt in poetry, creativity, peak experiences and deep love that has an ecstatic quality. It is the pearl beyond price that lies below and within our character faults (LO, pp. 34, 35), ego defenses, ignorance, and illusions that we often dwell on in our everyday consciousness.

The "core self" can register many painful feelings. It can also contain and own them in an almost unburdened way and let them pass as if floating down a river. Its common disposition is light heartedness, joy, and easy-going yet passionate engagement with others and life. It does not worry and fret and spoil good feelings as the lower self does.

The core self does not exist in the separated state of the little ego (LO, pp. 44-45, 48-49), in which it sees itself at war with the world in a constant zero-sum game. It is inclusive of others yet skillful enough in setting boundaries and protecting itself without, hate, revenge, triumph, or hubris. It uses loving assertiveness instead of revenge, healthy boundaries instead of attacks on others, and believes that what others have does not take away from its own inner wealth.

These thoughts about the core self, also often known as the "higher self" or "greater self" (LO, pp. 33, 38-40, 47) may cause some to recoil with thoughts like, "that's way beyond me or that sounds stilted and unrealistic." Well, it is, if you think I am saying this is how you are supposed to be and that if you aren't yet, you should be ashamed or guilty or self-condemning. I am saying this is your birthright that you can work toward. Probably none of us can exist and live our lives from our core self all the time, but we can spend much more of their lives embracing our core, seeking inspiration from within and living with more and more peace in our soul. I also do not want to put myself up as a paragon of core-self living, but I will say the more I have practiced what I suggest in the text and live from the unitive state, the more peace, joy, and creativity I have found in my life.

Factors That Block Us from Our Core Self

While we may believe on a conscious level that a quarrel is just a quarrel and has little real weight, when you check in with your unconscious a quarrel can often be felt to be a matter of life and death. This is so because when we are invested in our ego it is an investment in how we appear to others. From the position of the ego, being denied by others because we are wrong, or not on top, or best, or just not valued as much as we believe we need to be is experienced emotionally as death. Have you ever heard of the saying "A brave man dies but once, but a coward dies a thousand times?" Well, you don't have to be a coward to die a thousand times. We suffer the same fate when we are ego driven and need to be separate, better, above, or right. The denial by others is experienced in very much the same way as the coward's death. As we increasingly live from our core, we inexorably leave behind our ego investment in rightness in favor of love between us, truth that often exists on both sides, and positive outcomes. This heals the dualistic split and investment in a zero-sum outcome.

When you live from your core, neurotic symptoms begin to resolve naturally. Neurotic symptoms are the result of the ego's separateness and warring attitude with life. As we truly feel more deeply caring and loving toward others, rather than paying lip service to it, anxieties and depression recede. Depression is the warring attitude toward life turned on ourselves, and anxiety is a signal that our anger within will overwhelm us, or by way of projection onto others that they will criticize, condemn, or abandon us. Paranoia itself is a projection of our warring attitude toward others. I could make a list of all the turns that the warring attitude of the little ego and lower self take in psychopathology. The warring attitude does not exist in a psyche that lives from its core.

When one lives from the separated little ego, it creates a world experience of contention, constant battles, and war with the world and ourself. The paranoid attitude of the little ego that believes others always intend to defeat us so we must defeat them first, begins to create and foster a reality that we are at war. This is so because we start to posture in ways that threaten others. We act in hostile ways that provoke others' hostility and we grab and horde, which causes others to grab and horde.

When we live from the core self, we leave the warring attitude behind and begin to create a benign circle in life that promotes love around us and peace inside us. Living in peace within promotes peace without and a new reality accrues or, rather, we drop into the new reality. It is the ultimate reality of which mystics speak. There is the "real world" of the warring attitude that we live in most of the time. What we think of as the "real world" is actually the world of illusion, or duality. Contention, opposition, war with life are the illusions that we have created that become our temporary reality based on the warring ego. War between tribes, nations, religions, or creeds is the out-picturing of too many of us living in the collective dualistic illusion of a warring attitude.

Activity 1.1
Meditation to Connect with the Core Self
As we work through our irrational ideas, negative inner attitudes, selfishness, arrogance, and other negativities, we liberate the loving, expansive core self from its shackles. We become inspired by its energy, passion, excitement, joy, and love. We become vitalized, as it were, and we realize that we are part of great sea of benevolence that lies within. This is self-realization.

Right now, you can sit still and tune in quietly to your core self. First, go with the positive for a moment and imagine that it is there to get in touch with. Then set an intention to get in touch with the deepest, wisest, most secure, loving, and creative aspect of yourself.

Breathe out with long exhales, listen, and feel what comes. You may feel chatter or background noise. Let it go.

You may also have troublesome feelings or conflicts, as in imagined worries or battles with others. Note them so you can work on these conflicts at a later time, then let them go.

You may also experience wishful daydreams. Note them and let them go.

After a time, you will begin to feel moments of emptiness, if only for seconds. Let them be. Let the chatter, conflict, and daydreams go when they return and be with the emptiness.

The emptiness is a portal to your core; let it be for a while and feel its peace and dynamic stillness.

***

As you do this daily, you will begin to feel inspired from within. A new vitalized, creative power will become more prominent in your life and you will notice a greater peace.

Take the conflicts that you note and also recognize in your troubled reactions in your waking life to a *daily review* of yourself. It is best to do your daily review in the form of a written journal, but if you find this too hard then at least do a mental journal.

Ask yourself where these feelings or conflicts that you have noted have a source in your own creation. Where might you be fighting from a separated, fearful, or otherwise troubled position. Where does your own egoism, forcing current, low-frustration tolerance, and desire to blame others contribute to your trouble? Then make a commitment to at least attempt to live from kindness and inclusion instead of your faults.

This daily review of your contribution to your outer conflicts requires courage to accept your faults and responsibility for your life instead of finding fault with others and whitewashing yourself. It takes what I call negative capability, which is the ability to accept who you are now to open real doors to change.

As you work on yourself, listen for your emerging creativity and guidance that help heal divisiveness in your life. Look for inspiration and guidance that come to you by how events conspire to teach you more about yourself and open up possibilities of experience. Remember to honor your unique individual expression in your life. Your plan may not fit in with all the outer rules offered by the society around you. It may, but it may not. Honor your inner experience, guidance, and direction instead of relying on outer rules so much. Your life path may not be the same as others; believe in yourself.

Activity 1.2
Meditation to Find Your Unique Gifts
As you sit right now, let yourself be comfortable in your chair, with your spine straight without forcing. Concentrate on your breathing, and as you exhale let your thoughts go and allow yourself to become empty. Thoughts will come back in, but let them go again, creating a moment or two in which you feel somewhat calm and empty.

During this calm state, ask yourself: What are my unique gifts? What do I offer the world and what can I offer going forward? Be with that for a while. You will receive answers. Note them to yourself.

Next, let yourself register what fears or anxieties seem to arise when you get excited about your gifts. Note these inhibitions.

As you come to full awareness again, ask yourself what faults get in the way of your accepting or expanding your gifts. Some of your gifts may include your wisdom, kindness, or more concrete abilities like skills, organizational ability, financial acumen, and intelligence that you use to write or teach. Note your faults and fears that block the best in you.

Faults and fears: _____

_____

_____

_____

_____

_____

Are the faults your laziness, your fear, your pride? Is there a sense of being undeserving? Then imagine the opposite of your faults as also you. If you are blocked by fear, feel into your courage; if you feel lazy connect with your willpower; if you feel undeserving, connect with the part of you that wants to use your gifts to benefit others as well as yourself. Make notes of these positive impressions and set an intention to honor the positive elements in you and believe in them.

Many therapists do this all the time in their work. They reframe negative thoughts and help connect people with their strengths and positive qualities. The activity above is focused on connecting with the unique positive gifts that you possess and need to acknowledge for your emotional growth. It does not bypass your faults or lower self, as often happens when positive visualization is used. This activity is designed to help you take on and unsettle your faults and inhibitions that obstruct the connection with your core.

Activity 1.3
Meditation to Find Positive Answers for Problems
Here is another simple but powerful activity that helps connect you with your positive qualities and promotes a connection with your core.

Take any relationship conflict that you are in, large or small. Instead of seeing it just from your perspective, imagine the most constructive thing you could do to resolve this conflict. This will include trying to find some way for the other person to win to a degree. This may not be a meting out of your vengeance, triumphing over the other, or getting your way completely. Perhaps being constructive might involve being positively assertive rather than hostile. Try to let go of the spirit of war in your conflicts and replace it with peaceful negotiation when you engage. See and feel the humanity in the other as you speak.

Note a conflict: _____

_____

_____

_____

_____

Note the other's perspective:

_____

_____

_____

Note your perspective: _____

_____

_____

_____

_____

_____

_____

What is the most constructive way to understand the essence of the other's position and yours and make an assertive, non-hostile expression that accounts for both points of view that, hopefully, is healing? It should in most cases involve a win–win proposition.

_____

_____

_____

_____

_____

_____

_____

_____

_____

Chapter 2
Unity and Duality

The appreciation of the two concepts of unity and duality as differing ways of being in world can have profound effects on self-transformation. If you are employing self-analysis or self-examination as a way to grow emotionally or spiritually, the understanding of these concepts can help immensely. If you are a therapist who wishes to employ the concepts to help your client, these concepts can provide a powerful accelerant to your client's growth arc.

There are two fundamental planes of existence: the unitive plane and the plane of duality (LO pp. 11, 14-15, 43, 126, 129, 161, 164, 175). The unitive plane is the plane of reality beneath or within the outer illusory way of being in conflict with the world. It is the plane of existence that appreciates the equality of all others with ourself. On this plane, equality is felt as a fact, and because of that there is a great peace at this level of existence. The core self is the embodiment of the unitive plane of existence (LO, pp. 12, 43, 88, 128). The core self embodies the dual-track notion (LO, pp. 30, 35, 41) of the self being inherently self and other. It is the paradox that I am my own self with my own identity and yet simultaneously I am also the other. At this plane of existence, hurting the other is understood as tantamount to your right hand hurting your left hand; each is still *your* hand.

Since the core self, appreciated and accepted in the self or not, has a felt sense of the oneness of self and other—as we know our left hand like our right is still part of us—this felt sense of unity makes it seem crazy for us to see the other as someone who needs to be triumphed over or defeated. From this felt sense of unity, we realize we don't have to be more special, better than, higher, or glorified at another person's expense. At the risk of sounding excessively sentimental, the core self and the unitive plane exist on the plane of love, inclusion, and peace.

Having said that, most of us spend our time on the dualistic plane. This is the typical state of consciousness that sees the world as good or bad and as us versus them. Either I win, am heroic, and the opponent is vanquished, or I lose, and am totally defeated, worthless, and mortified. It is not the plane of the core self but rather the plane of the ego, which has to be separated and special to feel it has existence. The ego, bound by the sense of "I-ness" that excludes others, does not feel it is real and alive unless others value, esteem, and elevate it. If it sinks into non-distinction from others, it feels its very existence is in jeopardy. This is why even very small matters on the dualistic plane seem to be matters of life and death. Being right about even the smallest detail is critical, for then others will value and appreciate me, and I will feel safe. If I lose, then others will look down on me, think poorly of me, laugh at me, and feel contempt for me; then I am abandoned in their eyes, which means death.

Here is the very reason some mystics of various schools confuse the idea of giving up a separate identity altogether with giving up ego separateness and elevation. We all want to exist; no one wants to lose their identity. But if we give up our warring attitude—that the egos separate psychologically in terms of hubristic elevation above the other—then I am important and so is the other, and neither of us has to defeat the other or reign supreme over the other. This is the state of peace, or grace, or unity that we all long for, whether we are conscious of it or not.

Okay, so how do we work on this from a depth psychology perspective (LO, pp. 11, 14, 45, 126-127, 174)? How do we move from a dualistic to a more unitive perspective over the course of time? To begin with, we need to see the core self and the unitive state as a real possibility within us. It helps to hold it in mind consciously and long for it openly, at least to yourself. It helps to visualize this way of being in the world and the peace that is possible. So, make this a goal and part of your meditation each day. If you are a therapist working with a client, see if they are open to all the possibilities of wisdom, creativity, and peace and love that reside deep within them and encourage them to believe in themselves in this way. If they can't be open, then there is a great opportunity to have them vent their resistance to it and make conscious where it can be challenged.

More important, let's look at how duality can be psychologically accepted and challenged each day. Any daily problem, relational conflict, anxiety, depression, or disquietude has within it seeds of dualistic thinking that stem from the ego with its separateness and desire for personal elevation. The ego has to win each quarrel or debate or struggle in any psychological arena or its failure is experienced as death. If others don't think we are special, we are nothing; hence, our illusion is that we must win to be esteemed in others' eyes and thought of as special. From this perspective, a zero-sum game ensues. Either I win, or they do. Either I win and triumph and do the dance of superiority, or they win, and I am a worthless non-entity.

For example, a supervisee told me about a young man who had a very difficult time with his anger. He was prone to explosive outbursts that resulted in all kinds of relational problems. His most recent major outburst occurred when his dad was raising his voice and criticizing him. This young man seemed to have a problem with strong noises of any kind, so when his dad raised his voice the son became agitated and asked his father to lower it. Well, the father didn't like the idea of lowering his voice, so he continued at the same volume. The young man then became really angry and threw his plateful of food at the wall, smashing it, and cussed his father out all the way to his bedroom. Of course, the father didn't like this much, and the arguments increased. Let's just say that it didn't end well.

My supervisee was focused on how the client could communicate with this intractable father in such a way that the father would actually listen and respond by being nicer and quieter, which by the way he had never done. I suggested that the young man must have felt his father's refusal to listen to him and change as a huge defeat, which made the client feel he was devalued and unloved and therefore was a worthless piece of shit in his own eyes as well as his father's. So he exploded.

The answer to this dilemma was not getting the father to change but rather having the client let go of the need to win this battle with the father and let go of the false belief that his father's not caring enough to lower his voice meant that he was a worthless piece of shit. Rather, this is on the father. If the father is going to be an "ass," it doesn't mean the son has less worth. Understand that the father has his faults and if he doesn't change, it is on the father not the son.

This was a new tack that seems to help the supervisee out of this impasse. If the other person has to bend to our will, see it our way, and capitulate to us, then we are stuck. If we can give up insisting on having our way, be right, and win all the time, we step out of these conflicts. Sometimes we need to speak up for ourselves for our sake and the other's benefit. But when the ego is not so involved it doesn't seem like this life-and-death battle that results in explosions and/or relationship failure. Things are easier when we give up the ego stakes. It is actually easier to be assertive when we are doing it for the sake of the truth or the benefit of the self and other rather than for the defeat of and triumph over the other. Easiness, kind assertiveness, light-heartedness, peace, and joy are common attributes of operating from the core.

I run a large case consultation group for therapists who are developing their skills. Over a few weeks' time, I noticed that I was anxious for several groups in a row. I wondered about the anxiety and what it meant. I realized two things had occurred to make me more anxious. The first was that there were a few new therapists in the group that were pretty sharp and had their own ideas, and I was scared they would find realistic fault with some of my guidance and suggestions. The second thing that occurred, which compounded the first, was that a camera was brought into the room to record the work. Some of the recordings were being done for possible publication on YouTube for teaching purposes. This raised the stakes for me to be right, not make any mistakes, and be the "master clinician." It took a little digging to get there, and perhaps it should have been obvious, but there it was—my ego in all its "glory."

I felt into how important it seemed to be right, how I needed to run the show, how I had to have toppers to others' remarks. My feelings were tense and pushy. I really felt that if I didn't show I was "the best" in the group on camera, something frightening would happen. It was the abyss of illusion. I had to carry the show, or I would dissolve, be worthless, unimportant to others; they would turn away and then I would vanish.

Understanding this, I jumped into the experience in a different way. In my imagination, I entertained the idea of being wrong, making mistakes, and letting others shine more brightly. I began to feel a positive, easy feeling, which helped me have confidence. It was important for me to let go of what I thought I needed.

When the group came, I tried to let myself be acutely aware of how anxious I was. I practiced the opposite of repression—a rather hyper awareness and focus. I felt into my anxiety and how when others talked, I felt I had to be first, better, and more right. Then I contained myself and encouraged others to talk. I let them say more than I did and shine. Then the anxiety began to abate. I started to float with a sense of calmness. When I spoke, it wasn't urgent or pushy. Gone was the anxiety that told me if I wasn't on top, I was nothing.

I try to practice this every time I am in a large social situation or when I lead a group. The anxiety continues to swell when things begin but lessens as time goes by. And it abates more quickly as well.

Look into any relationship problem you have. See where you are too identified with your ego and have to be right and held as important in the other's eyes. See how deep down your feelings are out of proportion to reality. See how being wrong or not special is tantamount to death. In our deep psyche, even a small squabble can feel like a matter of life or death. I am right, or she is right. If she is right, I am doomed. See how this leads to a continued acceleration and amplification of squabbles and arguments, sometimes to the point of a breakdown in a relationship, especially if this happens frequently.

After you identify having to be right, better, or esteemed in a way the other is not prepared to do, hold it in your mind and body, breathe and jump into the abyss of illusion. Identify the fear that you will perish if you don't get the love, esteem, and valuing you are so desperate for from the other person. Breathe some more and let go and let these feelings be.

Then try to tell yourself that you don't need to win and try to step out of the fight. Take a time-out, bring in some humor, see the truth in the other's point of view. Let yourself float and not push, force, or strain to convince them. You will be okay. You will be more than okay the more you practice jumping into the abyss and letting go.

When we are identified with the core or real self that includes the other and refrains from seeing that our worth, value, and even existence depends on being right or better in the other's eyes, then we transcend the duality.

Let me also say at this point that letting go of the identification with the ego's separateness, its need to be special and elevated, has a tremendous positive effect on another existential psychological issue: death anxiety. As we can let the little ego apparently die by not having to be special or separate, and we can ease into a win–win approach to relationship and life, life becomes easier and more trustworthy. When we identify with our core self, which includes others, we move to unity with the "All." This movement expands our self-representation in a feeling way, and as we are with and within others and they within us, the continuity of life within us goes on.

Another effect of transcending duality and moving toward the unitive state is that since life becomes easier, we have less of an impulse to run away from it into the great exit door marked death. Life and death both become easier and safer.

What I am talking about here is a depth psychological practice that helps with the transcendence of duality. It is not some far away meditative state. It does not have to be reserved for mystics and monks. We all can move toward the peace and liberation that come with the liberation of the core self and the experience of the unitive state.

Look at your life and issues. See where you are bound to others' opinion of you. See how you feel you have to be loved, esteemed, and elevated by everyone around you or you fall into the abyss of worthlessness and psychic death. Please don't glibly turn away from this issue and say, "not me." It is quite universal. It is just a matter of how intensely we have this problem and how aware of it we are. To therapists who read this book, let me say that this applies to you and us, not just our clients. This is a human condition, not just a client condition.

Fear as a Defense

Many of the issues that keep us from our core and unnecessarily attached to the ego have to do with the major fault of pride. I do not mean healthy pride in ourselves like self-esteem, but rather the hubristic pride that is attached to self-elevation. This is part of the separation of the ego. It has to be away from, better, or more than the other, and glorified by those around us. The next major fault that entraps us in the ego and duality and keeps us from the core self and unitive state is fear. The notion that fear is a fault and not just an effect is a rather novel take on fear that is not often found in mundane psychology but can be found in mystical schools.

A hallmark of the core self and unitive state is the absence of fear. It is a joyful embrace of all living, including the joy and pain that comes our way and an acceptance of life on life's terms. When we are in fear, it cripples our ability to live fully and be the loving persons we all can be. I have already talked about how becoming aware of your ego and its separateness and tendency for self-elevation reduces our great existential fear of death. I would like to go further here into issues with the fear of life, commitment, and love. Love, the great liberating and empowering force in the universe, is feared when we are attached to the ego and self-will, compulsively needing to have things go our way. Love is felt to be a trap when we secretly try to dominate, win over, control, and triumph unconsciously over those we love. The angry dependency (LO, pp. 56, 131, 152) that accrues from fear, self-will, and pride causes us to shrink from our spontaneous impulse of loving others. This is so because unconsciously we believe others are just as invested in controlling, being better than, and triumphing over us as we unconsciously are toward them.

A way to deal with this fear of surrendering to the outreaching soul-current of love and our fear of being controlled and used up by others is to treat all of our fears as projections. Whenever you feel others are trying to control you, look into the ways you might be controlling. If you feel the other always has to be on top, look at the issue in yourself. If you believe others are trying to guilt-trip you, look into how you might be a guilt tripper. If you feel they are always trying to get their way, look into how you subtly push to get your way or have to convince others your way is the best way so you win out. Believe me, we all do these manipulations; they are a mirror to what we haven't faced yet in ourselves.

Here is another trick: Even if the other is being manipulative, self-righteous, forcing, or arrogant, if you discover where in yourself you are operating with these faults in the situation and you clean up your end of the trouble, the other person's faults are put into much greater relief over time. This relief or clarity makes their issues more obvious to both of you. When you don't react and they remain negative, it rather stares them in the face, so to speak. This is because you are not hooking in and reacting, which obscures who is really at fault. Maybe your troubles are almost all a result of your faults and projections. If this is so, you have an almost straight line to improvement and a loving relationship. If the other person's faults are the problem, when you clean up yours theirs will stick out, making them obvious to both of you.

A further benefit to understanding and transforming your faults that keep you away from your core self is that doing so frees you from your own guilty feelings that cause you to give in to others' demands. When you give in to the demands of others in a way that makes you feel defeated, dominated, or controlled, you remain fearful of true surrender to love. It is a sort of paradox, but loving surrender is different than "giving in" out of fear of defeat; rather it is consciously choosing to surrender when you feel it is a good thing to do. Giving in out of fear of losing control, loss, or defeat is just that: It is giving in to fear. When you are strong and loving, and you give over in relationship to others, it feels very different. You are not surrendering then out of fear but out of love.

Knowing your self is an important key here. If you know your faults of control, manipulation, and guilt tripping, for example, and contain them and begin to transform them, you stop being so vulnerable to these faults in the other. If you can feel your need for control and you check it and begin to say, "Right now, I am not going to do this. I am going to let this person be," it frees you. It frees you because when you know in an immediate way that it is not right for you to be controlling, you immediately know it's not right for your partner, or friend, or family member to control you. It becomes much easier then to speak up in a positive way and set your boundaries and say, "No I don't want to do that, thank you." The felt sense of the rightness of your "no" comes from allowing others the right to say "no" to you without receiving punishment or rejection from you. The same holds true with letting others be right, or first, or better in a given moment.

Activity 2.1
Meditation to Find Which of our Faults Contribute to Our Problems

Take a moment right now. Be still and sit quietly. Let go of thoughts that come, and, as you exhale, relax. When you find a moment of peace, think about an issue you are having with a relationship—something that always causes uneasiness or strife. Think it over a bit, then ask yourself, "What are my faults in this troubled situation?" Does the world have to fit my structured ideas? Does the other person have to see the light and see things my way for me to be at peace? Do I have to be right, or first, or on top?

Issue: _____

My faults: _____

_____

_____

Feel into the issue from your fear and your faults that it has to be "my way, as I see it, me first," and try to let it go. Try to feel into a place where you don't have to win. Breathe in and feel yourself begin to fall and then float in this abyss of illusion—that if things are not as I see them, I am in danger. The universe is ultimately truly benevolent; our warring attitude in daily life makes it a fearful and sometimes dangerous place on the level of dualistic reality.

***

Back to the beginning of this section: Take into account that fear is a fault not just an artifact. It keeps us from the embodiment of unitive consciousness—the core self, with all its joy and peace. Look at your life and your goals. Anything you do because you want to avoid something out of fear is problematic. If you want a love relationship because you fear being alone, it is a problem; work on your fear of loneliness. If you want success because you fear failure, work on your fear of failure. If you need to be right because you can't stand to be wrong, work on your fear of being wrong. If you cling to life out of fear of the dying process, let yourself die into the abyss of illusion.

So many times people come to me with only their conscious experience of needing something or wanting something in their lives. They say, "I just want a relationship, or I just want to be happy." I don't doubt for a minute that they want a relationship, or they want to be happy. What I do doubt is the "just" part. If we entirely wanted and were committed to being happy or to a relationship, or success, or anything positive within reason, we would have it. The problem that keeps us away from these good things, including peace and joy, is that there is part of us that doesn't want it. You may think "that Sollars is crazy," but I tell you it is so. Success, happiness, joy, peace—they all have been contaminated with our illusions and defenses so that unconsciously we are afraid of these positive things or we believe the price to pay for them is too high. If 90 percent of us "just" wants the positive but even 10 percent of us doesn't, and especially if that 10 percent is unconscious, it will spoil the positive that we are looking for.

There are many reasons for this fear of the best in us and the best around us. Sometimes we don't want to pay the rightful price for something we wish. This is often because of a silent forcing current underneath a desire that thinks we should just have something bestowed on us with no effort. For example, it is hard to be a doctor or a lawyer or a teacher if you don't work hard and get your degrees. It is hard to develop a successful business if you don't fight for it in a positive way by learning, trial and error, and investment. If you don't want to make these kinds of investments of time, money, and energy, you are living in a rather illusory world of entitlement.

Here is another issue that makes us fear positive things in our life. Often, we may assume that the positive is dangerous because secretly we feel undeserving. We may feel it is dangerous because others may envy and hate us, and even want to harm us if we attain the positive. We feel this because we secretly harbor these kinds of attitudes ourselves and project them onto others.

Here is still another reason that we fear good things in our lives. If we are unconsciously unloving and negativistic toward others, we may unconsciously feel that we deserve punishment for the "unconscious crimes" of our own unlovingness. This may sound strange, but Freud noticed it over 100 years go and called it the need for punishment. He felt it was common in the human psyche to have this need for punishment because we have unconscious destructiveness and aggression. I call it unconscious unlovingness. Sometimes even emotional stinginess or withholding or contempt, for example, make us feel we should be punished and that we are undeserving of love and happiness.

I had a client who was a crafter; she mostly made pots and vases. I thought some of her work was very good, and she was able to make some money from it. When she was steeped in her own envy and spite, she was very afraid to show her art in public for fear of being attacked verbally or even physically. At her deepest unconscious level, she felt a group of people would gang up on her and attack and kill her if she was very successful. As she worked through her own envy, spite, and anger over a few years, she was finally able to display her art and became a moderate success. We have to look at the man or woman in the mirror if we want to free ourselves of the fear of the positive and the negative.

Often, the more we fervently want something, such as success, a relationship, or a good life, the more we say an unconscious "no" to what we consciously want. The intensity of the demand or need for the desired goal gives away the underlying "no" to it, if we are alert. When you believe that you "only and just" want the good and the positive, you will never see your "no" to your own desired fulfillment. In some measure, *we all want what we don't want and don't want what we want.* Very seldom is our psyche in complete unity regarding a goal or outcome, or we would have it with relative ease. Or it would be a goal or state that we have already and perhaps take for granted.

Activity 2.2
Meditation to Find Your No-Current
Take a moment right now, close your eyes, breathe deeply with long exhales. Quiet your mind and look at something you fervently want in your life: love, success, a reduction in anxiety, peace. Ask yourself: Why might I not want to attain this?" Write down your "no" to your want or need. Why might you be afraid or not want to pay the price? There may be several reasons that funnel into your no-current that work against your fulfillment. Try to be uncompromisingly honest about your "no."

What do I fervently want?

_____

_____

_____

Why might I not want to attain this positive thing?

_____

_____

_____

When you note a few things, such as I am afraid of it for this and that reason, or I don't want to pay the price for a particular reason, take them to your meditations. Ask yourself if you really want to say "no" to what you want. Paradoxically, keep bringing out the "no" and answer it with your core self.

***

Keep the no-current and the longing in juxtaposition. Over time, bring out your "no" and answer it until you wear the "no" down with your overall longing, commitment, and, most important, your core self. This requires continued practice over time, repeating the bringing out of your "no" and challenging it until the goal seems less frightening and more attainable.

Narcissism versus Healthy Self-Love

The inclusive, embracing, unifying love of the core self should never be confused with neurotic self-love of a narcissistic nature. Neurotic self-love is kind of an adoration of the self and attention seeking hidden within a preoccupation with the self. This preoccupation with the self is based on an inner weakness and dependency. It is not that the person with neurotic self-love or narcissism really loves themselves; rather, it is a feeling that they have to make a display of themselves or force others to love or admire them in an attempt to assuage their true lack of self-love and care.

Narcissism is really a ball and chain. It says "everyone must love me always." It keeps us outer-focused and in our forcing current to constantly garner love instead of just being for ourselves with a care that emerges from our depths, our core. People who relate from their core continually free themselves of their dependent need for love and replace it with an ability to love others as well as the self. As we learn how to love others, the need to have others love us recedes because a truly loving person feels good about themself; they like and love themself automatically, and a positive cycle replaces a dependent, negative one. I love; therefore, I like myself; therefore. I don't need other people to like or love or admire me so much; therefore, I can let others feel about me as they wish. It is the vicious-circle counterpart I describe as the Promethean chain in Chapter 3 of *Love Outraged.*

There is another kind of narcissism that does not have the idealized overlay of love that is part of the "positive narcissist" who garners attention through self-inflation, drama, and a puffed-up quality. That is the depleted narcissist. The depleted narcissist makes no pretense of dramatics, theatrics, or hyperbole but rather presents as a needy person who is anxious and looking to please. This person usually makes use of the distortion of love that is masochistic submission, self-denial, and ingratiation. This person is a people pleaser, at least for the sake of appearances, but harbors a hidden forcing current to coerce others to love them by attempting to induce guilt, concern, and care by seduction and submission. The depleted narcissist can seem like a loving person, but their self-denial has an unwholesome quality that often causes people to avoid them or sometimes just exploit them. They operate from the mask of love but often harbor angry dependent feelings that cause anxiety and brooding.

The third narcissistic position, false serenity, involves someone who possesses self-love and an apparent lack of need for approval from others. This position is often the most difficult to spot in others and accept in ourselves. This is the person who presents an idealized image of composure. This person uses withdrawal and dampening of emotions to appear unaffected by life. The problem here is that the composure is an affectation and a defense rather than true serenity. Falsely serene people can pull off the appearance of serenity with others and even with themselves. They try very hard, albeit mostly unconsciously, to be unaffected by their needs, desires, and difficulties that pass their way. When troubled waters rise, they are unable to retain their composure and resort to anger, control, guilt tripping, or emotional seduction to get others to do their bidding.

This position resembles the unitive state, but it is only partially earned, and these narcissists live in the mask of serenity rather than really being it. They aren't as at peace as they present, and their mask shatters with stress or deprivation of any type, such as someone disagreeing with them or not getting their way, or loss of love of any sort. Like the narcissist with hidden depletion, demands for love and attention, and angry dependency, this false serene type's true colors will show when they don't get their way, or the needs become too pressing.

Having characterized these as types of personalities, I must quickly warn that things are not always so neat. Many times, we use an admixture of styles and masks even though we may predominantly resort to seduction or guilt tripping, as an example. When emotional seduction and guilt tripping don't work, the person may then default to angry demands and control.

The strong demand for love or admiration from others, however hidden, contains a forcing current that tries to make others and life do our bidding rather than accept others and life on their own terms. This forcing current is what Buddhists mean by desire that needs to be relinquished. I don't believe, as some do, that peace means having no desire. Having no desire is a withdrawal from life that would leave one depressed. However, desire should be easy, flowing, and should always contain an ability to take "no" for answer from life or others.

We also need attachment, although attachment in some circles has a bad name. Let me discuss healthy attachment and non-attachment. Attachment theorists have made a living helping us understand how important healthy attachment is in infancy and adulthood. Non-attachment in mystical circles means not being a slave to our attachments to others, materialism, or even life as we know it. Non-attachment means not selling your soul to acquire anything. It means self-composure and an ability to let go of demands and allow for the frustration of our needs without fearing self-annihilation.

Healthy attachment in adulthood provides for our psychological well-being through the love exchanged between two or more people. If a healthy attachment is ruptured through loss or death, or moving, or people growing away from one another, a healthy person will develop new attachments. The key will be that the emotional life and death of two adults does not depend on the other. Love is valued, nurturing is valued, kindness is valued. But we don't need to be desperate in each moment for a particular need to be met. This is healthy non-attachment as well as attachment.

The Abyss of Illusion

The intense neurotic desire for needs to be met, the angry dependency, the dependent attachment, and the forcing and demanding of life to do our bidding are contingent on what Eva Pierrakos (LO, pp. 6, 15, 38, 43) called the "abyss of illusion." The abyss is the sense of apparent doom we retreat from when we fear making a mistake, not getting our way, people not thinking we are special, fearing others lack emotional availability, or life requiring effort. All the irrational ideas organize around this illusion. The belief is that if I am not loved always and by everyone, I cannot stand it; I have to be more admired and special than others; I have to get my way in all things; if I am not perfect, I am nobody; life has to be easy and provide for all my needs or I deserve to be angry and punishing; so everyone around me needs to believe I am first, better and more special, or I am nothing.

Here is the immediate dilemma for anyone reading these particular words on the abyss of illusion and our irrational demands. We all pay lip service to them as problems. We mostly, in glib fashion, say to ourselves that we are past these faults and dependencies. If you really look inside, you will see for certain that you are only partially free of these issues. You may have worked on your pride and your need to be special, or your having to be right; however, don't be fooled that you are done. The work of eroding and transforming these faults and the abyss will never be completely finished. These faults are in play whenever we are anxious, depressed, irrationally fearful, or phobic. If you are not at peace, you are under the influence of the abyss of illusion.

We do not have to completely resolve the abyss to feel better and grow into the more unitive state. As we do the work each day, or maybe each week, or when we feel problems or issues pop up, or when we help clients confront the abyss, the work liberates pleasure and joy. One can feel the movement toward peace, acceptance, and relaxation as we progress. The more we do to challenge the abyss, the better we feel. The abyss of illusion is to a large extent responsible for our entrapment in duality. The work on the abyss liberates the core self and drops us into the unitive state. Jumping into the abyss does not mean falling into the void, although we think it is; it is falling into the unitive state. We have to go through the illusion in a concerted way, day after day, until we begin to feel the all-abiding peace that we look for on our spiritual journey and in counseling.

Activity 2.3
Meditation to Unmask Ego Fears
Take any problem or anxiety you have. Try to feel into the problem to discover the abyss in you where you feel your doom awaits if you are not first, more special, or if your ego is threatened that you might make a mistake. Write down which fault or irrational idea is involved with your worry, anxiety, or brooding about something already past. Put it on paper or on your computer and see it there in black and

white. Breathe and feel into the fear. Finally, ask yourself questions like:

- Do I really have to be loved or admired here to feel okay?
- Do I have to be first or best to be okay?
- If I make a mistake in this situation, is it really as tragic as I imagine?
- If the other person becomes mad at me, does this really have to crush me and result in a need for revenge?
- If I am not perfect, will I really die this imaginary death like I imagine?

If you really engage with these questions, even just reading them will probably give you some relief from the troubles that rob you of your peace and keep you away from your core self.

***

Activity 2.4
Daily Review to Help Resolve Trouble Spots in Your Life

Another thing you can do is to try to keep a journal, and every day review trouble spots and times when you overreacted or felt irrationally frightened. Write down the situation and look for the abyss and your sense that you had to have your way, or couldn't be wrong, or couldn't accept a human failing in yourself. Note it on paper, then go back to feeling into your abyss of illusion and jump into it to see if you don't float after you drop for a second. See if your fears don't begin to recede. Then see if you can begin to practice daily letting go and dropping in when you are scared at work, or with friends, or even when your own mind imagines a future "disaster" or illusory emotional death. As you use your review daily, you will begin to feel more peaceful, more loving; conflicts will begin to reveal solutions, and you will love from your core more substantially and feel the peace of the unitive state behind your illusions.

Total Responsibility

Another requirement to live from your core self is the acceptance of total responsibility for your life. If you focus on blaming others, life, or circumstances for your problems, you are lost to begin with. Find your way back home to responsibility for your life and situation. You do not need to be a mystic to appreciate total responsibility for your life. Existentialists talk about this, as does anyone with great integrity who takes command of their life.

If you remain bent on being mad because life doesn't provide you with opportunity, or you blame other people for creating your problems, you are very stuck. What can begin to set you free is taking total responsibility for your plight and your life. Don't think you need this or that worldly thing or accomplishment to be happy. Happiness comes from accepting responsibility and making a commitment to accept life on life's terms. It doesn't mean being passive. We need to do what we can to grow emotionally, and as we do happiness is a by-product.

Let's look at a common situation in which a person lacks good friends. They may feel they can't be happy unless they make more friends. Instead of blaming others or life for feeling lonely and the lack of friends, they might gain some friends if they would ask themselves questions about what might be turning people away. What could I be doing differently? Do I have faults that drive people away? Am I pushy, or selfish in hidden ways, or narcissistic and subtly demand that others pay attention to and focus on me out of proportion to others? Do I have to always be right, be on top, be the winner, be more special than the next person? If you have these traits and you connect the dots, you can begin to see some of the causes for your loneliness.

Depressed people are usually mad at life. They most often deny it to themselves and others because they want to appear "nice" and giving, and as if they just have sad feelings about their plight. But it is not the sadness in most cases that is the problem. The ultimate problem is their anger at life for being difficult, with the aggression turned on themselves. The depression and self-preoccupation are also an attack on life and others around them—sometimes also God. They want to punish others in order for others or life to be better "mothers" and make life better for them and take away their pain. Even if depression is related to loss or grief, it is not true sadness that causes the depression; it is the bitter, hard anger with life for not being perfect and easy and protecting them from every pain.

If anyone looks into their depression honestly without self-deception, they will find this punishment of life and others because they believe others have not done "right by them." A person who embraces self-responsibility will quickly see within themselves their punishing attitude and challenge it, and their depression will abate rather quickly.

If you feel unsuccessful, underemployed, or as if life is passing you by, you can either blame life, or you can look more deeply at the part of you that perhaps fears success. Maybe you may find that you are spiteful about reaching for success because it may not be the grand success you had wanted and demanded out of life. If life is not the whole loaf of bread, you won't buy it. You won't settle for the half loaf; "nope not me, all or none."

I had one person that I worked with say to me with great intensity, "if I am not first, I am nothing." Well, he didn't do very well in life in the end because he couldn't shake this belief. A person who is responsible for him- or herself will realize they are the cause of their own lack of success, unhappiness, or unfulfillment and make the best possible choice to have the best they can in life. People who are bitter and externalize blame will choose spite and self-pity over the constructive alternative.

People who don't take full responsibility for their lives remain tethered and dependent. The fact that they make others and life responsible takes away their power. Victims always give away their power. Instead of looking inward and making changes to maximize their life and fulfillment, they would rather enjoy their spite, self-pity, and bitter envy. But what a price there is to pay. A vicious negative cycle is created that leads to further and further blame, negativity, unhappiness, and emotional enslavement. This remains unless at some point they begin to free themselves from the bondage of blame and the abdication of self-responsibility.

Chapter 3
The Model

The personality theory suggested with this approach is drawn from the mystical schools of the Kabala, Gnosticism, Sufism, Taoism, Buddhism, and Hinduism and viewed through a psychoanalytic lens. The visual of the cosmic egg is a big help in illustrating the personality in pictorial form (see Figure 1). The personality has four different self-elements represented in the figure. The four elements consist of the core self, the lower self, the ego, and the false self. The core self (LO, pp. 10,12-13,19-22, 25, 29, 31-33, 39-40)—illustrated as the centermost element in the figure, is the deepest level of our personality. Within the core self, there is a faint image of the Taoist Yin Yang, symbolizing unitive consciousness. The core self is surrounded by the lower self (LO, pp. 40, 44-47, 53, 55, 59-60, 1690)—represented by the center portion of the egg—which contains the personality's character faults, conscious and unconscious negativity, and negative inner will. The ego (LO, pp 12-13, 30, 44-45, 48-49, 51)—illustrated by the darker grey in the middle portion of the egg—shrouds both the lower self and the core self but can also become part of the lower self at times. The ego represents decision-making functions and commonly understood capacities such as judgment, discernment, and will. The false self, or mask (LO, pp. 53-54, 59, 132, 134, 156, 166)—depicted by the lighter grey near the point of the egg—shrouds the ego, the lower self, and the core. The false self represents a façade of what it thinks is the best image it can present to the world based on inner fears and aggression. The goal of spiritual/psychological work from this perspective is to transform the negative aspects of the false self, ego, and lower self back into the peaceful, loving, creative, outpouring, and wise core self.

The Personality Illustrated from a Spiritual Perspective in the Form of the Cosmic Egg

Figure 1

The negative character traits, and pretenses are distortions of the loving expression of the core self; they are love outraged (LO, pp. 6, 33-34, 45-46, 50, 56, 102, 107, 113, 126, 54, 162, 164, 167, 172). Once these negative aspects are understood and worked through, they eventually revert to the positive, loving qualities of the core self through psychological transformation.

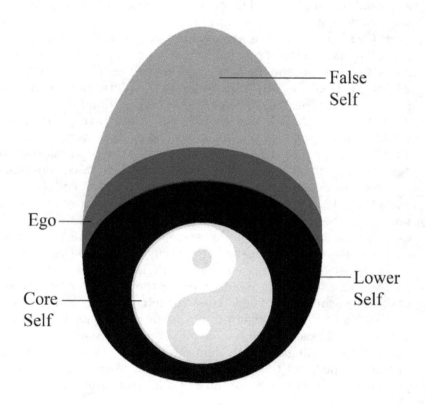

Artwork by Janis Glotkowski, MA, TLLP

The lower self develops as we go through life's difficulties and the positive attributes of our core self become deadened and defended against, especially when a growing individual experiences early trauma. Then the desire for love may become overthrown and displaced or converted into its opposites such as hate and envy. Throughout our development, the better parenting and social support we receive, the more our loving qualities will blossom instead of becoming deadened or distorted into negativity traits or qualities. Biological fragility such as a genetic propensity for mental illness makes the personality more vulnerable to psychic injury and more prone to be defended against by a false or lower self.

The Core Self

The core self, which is also known as the higher self (LO, pp. 33, 38-40, 47) in many spiritual and philosophical teachings, is the deepest aspect of the personality. It is the pearl beyond price or the divine spark (LO, pp. 39, 161) within us. All other personality elements are derivations of the core self. It is the loving, wise and transpersonal element of the personality that is connected with others, the environment, and the planet in a unitive way. Unitive meaning. in this case, is a true level of reality that underlies all the separateness we experience in our everyday lives. From this level of experience, we are not at war with anyone or anything but truly appreciate our oneness and common bond with everything.

The world we normally experience, the world of duality, is considered an illusion, while the deeper, real world is far more benevolent; this is unitive consciousness where the core self is found. Jesus says that the Kingdom of God is within us. This is the core self, which is paradoxically one with the others and the planet and uniquely an individual self. If you have trouble with all this philosophically, just think of the core self as the deepest element of the personality that is loving, kind and wise.

People ask me about the core self. Is it love? Is it a self or a process? If it is love, how can it be a process? These difficult questions arise from what we call in philosophy "identitarian thinking"—that is, *things have to be only what they are and not what they aren't*. Paradoxically, on deeper levels of experience, *things can be what they are not and not what they are*. These ideas are being confirmed by the newer science of quantum physics. We are discovering that things can be in two different places at one time, that light can be both a wave and particle at the same time, that events can have effects on far distance things with no time passing in-between. The core self can be both self and other, both at one with everything and self-contained, simultaneously love and personal identity.

The core self is the fountain of our personality. It's the fire and the fuel, the inspiration and the guidance that propels us through life. It is the life force (LO, pp. 13-14, 49, 51, 62, 71, 75, 165) itself, which also contains transpersonal wisdom that comes to us from beyond our rational modes of consciousness.

The aim of mystical expansion is to access the inspiration of the core self's consciousness. This book is designed as one way of working to liberate this powerful inspiration and guidance.

The Lower Self

The aspects of our personality that become distorted and misdirected, turning love into hate, avarice, cruelty, or envy is known as the lower self. The lower self is also known as the shadow (LO, pp. 38, 46-47, 55, 81, 113, 139, 140); this is a term coined by famous Swiss Psychiatrist Carl Jung, that refers to aspects of ourselves that we are unaware of and are mostly negative. Furthermore, the elements of the shadow are against the best interest and well-being of others and ourselves.

Childhood hurts and troubles cause psychic pain, leading to hurt and unpleasant feelings such as guilt and shame. These hurts cause the child's longing for love to become outraged, with this outrage turning into negative feelings, defenses, and character faults. Any negative, malicious aspect of the low self is what we are referring to as love outraged.

The lower self eventually develops a will of its own, which will be discussed in greater detail later in this workbook. It functions as a partially organized intentionality to defeat the best in us and life from a paranoid position that we have to be against others and at war with life to protect ourselves. Of course, as we believe so shall we create, so the lower self partially creates the actual world around us as well as our belief system.

To better understand how the lower self may create our negative world, think of someone who is paranoid. This person, believing others actually don't like him and have negative feelings toward him, may act angry as a defense. He may reject and be critical of the person he believes is negative toward him. This punishing attitude as a defense then actually creates angry and negative feelings toward him from the other where there wasn't any to begin with. Thus, a psychological prophecy is fulfilled, and the man is in a battle where there wasn't one before.

The Development of Character Faults as a Form of Lower Self Unconscious Negativity

When children are hurt through abuse, neglect, simple misunderstanding, or normal challenges in development, they do not simply feel sad and then move on. This hurt lasts a lot longer than a quick moment; more important, the hurt causes anger. This anger turns into what we call faults. These faults then strengthen all the bad feelings that we have about ourselves, making us feel guilty and that we do not deserve good things. As we grow older these faults also grow and make up a large part of what is considered our lower selves. There are many different faults that are harmful to ideal personality development. These faults, our negative feelings, and negative will are important in the liberation of our core self. Some of the major negative faults are further explored in detail to provide better understanding.

Envy

Envy (LO, pp. 56, 59, 70, 112, 187) occurs when someone has a desire or longing for something that someone else has such as an object or quality. When a child reaches out for love from an important figure in their life and does not receive it to the extent they desire, it creates pain. When a child longs for love long enough and gets nothing or very little in return, this pain turns into indifference and even hate. The indifference can be seen when children start to turn away from their longing or seek out love. When this gets very bad, they do not go out of their way to seek love in any form, such as attention or affection, from others. For example, if a young child, desires the relationship that the mother has with another sibling but is not able to fulfill this desire, she may become envious of the relationship. Because of the pain she is feeling, she may begin to tell herself that she does not care whether she has this relationship with her mother and may become cool, rejecting, or indifferent. By believing she does not care about the relationship, she can numb some of her pain.

When a child can no longer endure rejection passively—by being indifferent—they turn to hate as a defense mechanism. The child begins to hate the rejecter, expelling them from their need base to make the pain of rejection tolerable. When envy becomes hate, the relationship between the child and parent does not go away; rather, the connection is just of a different kind. This new connection of hate somewhat diminishes the longing and pain caused by the envy. Using the example from above, when a child is no longer able to use the defense mechanism of indifference, she may begin to use love's opposite—hate—as a defense mechanism. She may start to feel that she hates her mother and the relationship she has with her sibling.

Envy also contains hate in the form of wanting to spoil something about the person who is envied. In childhood, the first object of envy according to Melanie Klein (LO, p. 56), is the mother. The child longs for all the good that the mother should offer, and when this longing is frustrated and the child does not feel it is receiving all the "goodness" it desires, it attempts to spoil the good qualities in the mother. By spoiling the mother, the child is attempting to destroy the goodness that it feels it is not receiving, so as to not feel pain. In this form of hate, the child may also attempt to ruin the relationship her mother has with her sibling. She may go about this in many ways, but the end goal is to spoil what she is missing—the relationship with her mother—until it is so degraded that it is no longer there to be missed.

Envy is seen everywhere and is something that all human beings have; some do not have a lot of envy and others have so much envy that it becomes toxic. We are not always aware of our envy, but regardless of whether we are aware of it, the more envy we have the more problems we have. When envy is put into words it is saying, "I want what you have but I cannot get it. If I cannot get what you have, then I am going to act like I do not care, act like I do not want it, or destroy it. Then maybe I won't feel the pain of not being able to have what I desire." Perhaps if you think of the "sour grapes" fable, it will bring the nature of this fault home.

Activity 3.1
Transforming Your Envy

Think of a time when you were envious and responded with indifference, hate, and spoiling as a defense. Describe your thoughts, actions, and feelings. For example, when the child described above was using indifference, she might state, "I wish I had the same relationship that you have with my sibling, but since I don't, and I can't seem to get it, I am going to act like I do not care, although I do." Relax, be still; breathe in for a slow count of 5, breathe out for a slow count of 5. Think of the time when you felt envy and after moment write down your experiences next to the prompts below.

Envy–indifference:

_____

_____

Envy–hate:

_____

_____

Envy-spoiling:

_____

_____

***

After you do this, try to be still again and get in touch with the pain of not having what you longed for—the love, the admiration, the esteem. Then tell yourself you also admire these traits or accomplishments you wish to spoil. Breathe in and send an affirmation out to the ether that you wish the best for the person you were envious of, that you will do your best to fulfill your own potential and do not need to compare yourself to them any longer.

Spite

Spite (LO, pp. 56) occurs when one has the desire to deliberately hurt or upset someone regardless of the harm it may cause oneself or others around. Children use spite as a tool to get their parent or caregiver authorities to act how they want them to. When children feel hurt, they may act out of spite as a way of communicating with their parent that they were hurt. For example, if a parent leaves a child for a long time, the child will feel abandoned and hurt. When the parent returns, the child will want love and affection from the parent but will not act this way. They will act as if they do not want the parent around in a way to convey all the pain they have been feeling. If this spite was described in words ,the child would be saying to the parent, "If you leave again, even though I will be denying myself, I will punish you by withholding, withdrawing, or getting into some trouble that will cause everyone to be disturbed.

When I was a child of 7 or 8 and felt unduly punished in a squabble with my younger sister, I crawled under my father's bed to take my time out. I then noticed the electric cord to his radio lying on the floor. I somehow had a little pair of scissors, although I don't know where I got them, and I cut the cord to spite him. I received a strong shock as I thought I would, but I didn't care. Only later did the guilt set in for what I had done, along with my sore fingers. I still regret my act to this day.

Spite has never been eradicated from my personality, I am simply more aware of how often I feel it and talk myself out of it more frequently. It is a kind of a revenge move with a desire to punish. I feel spite when things don't go my way, or I feel embarrassed, hurt, or ashamed. I find spite bubbling up most every day, talk myself out of it, and try to lovingly stop myself from acting it out.

Activity 3.2:
Meditation to Raise Awareness of Spite

Be still again. Use your count of 5 to breathe in, and count of 5 to breathe out, a few times. Then think of a time when you were spiteful as a defense, or to punish someone, or how you currently feel spiteful. Describe your thoughts, actions, and feelings. Put them into words.

Event that evoked spite:

_____

_____

Feelings underneath spite: e.g., hurt, shame, embarrassment, sense of injustice:

_____

_____

Spite:

_____

_____

Now try to feel into the underlying feelings such as hurt, pain, embarrassment. Feel them for a while. Then think of a way you can speak about your feelings constructively and assertively, find a win–win approach to addressing your feelings in a relationship, or just talk them out with a friend. Finally, affirm that you are okay without acting out the spite. Breathe out and let it go.

***

Contempt

Contempt (LO, pp. 56-57) occurs when a person likes to feel that someone is beneath them and, therefore, disregards their being worthy. We use contempt to elevate ourselves and make us feel better when we feel bad about ourselves. This is a kind of identifying with the persecutor or rejecter. When we experience rejection from others, we may believe that if we act in the same way we will feel better about ourselves. By treating others with disrespect and acting as if they are not worthy or as good as us, it gives us the idea that we are better than they. Furthermore, we no longer view ourselves badly, because we have created someone "worse" than we are. Often, if we have a parent who is rejecting and contemptuous, we may identify with that parent and become rejecting and contemptuous ourselves.

As children, we desire love from our parent, but if our parent is rejecting, we do not receive this love. We relate our desire for love from this parent to their rejection and contempt. Consequently, we develop the belief that if we are rejecting and contemptuous to others than they will desire love from us the same way we did with the rejecting parent. We may also become like the rejecting parent because we want to avoid abuse from the rejecter and believe that it can be avoided if we become like them, and, in a sense, join their team.

Being contemptuous in this way is comparable to saying to someone "I have been put down in the past and feel bad about myself, so I am going to do the same to you in the hope that I will then feel better. Since I always desired love from those who were contemptuous of me, I am going to be contemptuous of you so that you then desire love and admiration from me. If I am the rejecter and dispel the hurt onto others, then I do not have to feel pain anymore."

Activity 3.3
Unsettling Contempt

Be still and do your breathing exercises. Think of times you were or are contemptuous of others. Feel in to the contemptuousness as a defense to make yourself feel better, to make others desire your love, and to avoid being rejected further. Describe your thoughts, actions, and feelings.

Contempt to make yourself feel better:

_____

_____

Contempt to make others desire your love:

_____

_____

Contempt to avoid further rejection:

_____

_____

Now, if you are able to find contempt within yourself, check in and see if you can detect how the contempt does not really accomplish safety but rather ego inflation that brings with it fear. Sense how this creates a cramp in your psyche that makes you fear retaliation and furthers feelings of a war-like mentality. Just breathe into your awareness and be with it for a moment.

***

Arrogance, Vanity, and Perfectionism

Arrogance is having an exaggerated belief in one's importance and ability. Vanity is being excessively proud of oneself and needing the admiration of others. Arrogance and vanity (LO, pp. 57) are both ways in which individuals try to raise themselves up above others and stem from attempts to resolve feelings of inferiority. Perfectionism (LO, pp. 57-58), which is much like egoism, is another defense mechanism that we use to resolve feelings of inferiority and self-doubt. When we feel that we have failed and that all other previous solutions have not worked, we feel inadequate and experience pain. By default, we then resort to the solution of becoming perfect, believing that if we can become perfect we will diminish our pain, inadequacies, and self-doubts and be lovable.

Using the defense mechanism of perfectionism as a strategy is bound to fail because perfectionism is not something that is ever attainable. When we try to become perfect, we end up with even more pain, self-doubt, and self-contempt because we were not able to achieve the standard we set for ourselves. Expecting yourself to be perfect at one thing is impossible, and once we realize that we are not able to achieve this standard of perfectionism, we set ourselves up for even more failure by deciding we need to become perfect in many different areas.

We want to be the best at everything—the smartest, the richest, the most popular. We strain, and strain, which brings ever greater anxiety that we might fail. Our intentions to be the best at everything are unrealistic, often contradictory, and do the opposite of what we are intending to do: decrease our inadequacies and self-doubt. For example, Drew wants to be the best father, the most successful businessman, the smartest, and the most well-liked. Is it possible for him to become perfect in these areas?

Activity 3.4
Exercise to Explore Consequences of Perfectionism

Explore the idea of perfectionism in the areas in the following example. Then think of areas where you strive for perfection but are unable to reach it because perfectionism in these areas is unrealistic and contradictory.

Example 1. If a person must be the most successful businessman, then he must spend all his time at work and away from his family, causing him to fail at being the best dad.

Example 2. If a person must be the smartest person there is, then he will annoy people by always having to be right and correct others, causing him to fail at being the most well-liked.

1. If I am _____, then I _____,

    causing me to fail at _____.

2. If I am _____, then I _____,

    causing me to fail at _____.

3. If I am _____, then I _____,

    causing me to fail at _____.

***

Along with perfectionism being unrealistic and contradictory, a bigger problem is that perfectionism is not a realistic relief for self-contempt. Being perfect and feeling accomplished does feel good; however, it does not resolve the reason that you desired perfectionism in the first place, which is that deep down you feel as if you are unlovable because you are not loving to others. Perfectionism entails feeling we are better than others; our need for triumph over others causes us to feel guilty. Our perfectionism then leaves us with guilt about all of our accomplishments because we feel as if we have reached this accomplishment at the expense of others. If you are the best at something, it means that everyone else is below you and that they will feel as if they are not as good as you.

Finally, perfectionism causes us to moralize about ourselves and others, destroying our self-esteem. We are never able to become perfect in our moral behavior and achievements, which causes us to lose confidence in our worth and abilities. The same way we moralize about our own inability to live up to the perfectionistic standard that we have set, we also moralize regarding others. We judge others contemptuously because they are unable to live up to the unrealistic standards that we have. Striving for perfectionism in ourselves and being judgmental to those whom we do not view as perfect does not help our self-esteem. Instead of feeling confident in ourselves and that we are a good person, we feel inadequate, unloving, and judgmental. Since we do not view ourselves as a good person, we do not feel that we are deserving of love, kindness, and fulfillment.

Using perfectionism as a defense mechanism is as if you were saying, "I feel inadequate because of my failures so I am going to try to be perfect. Even though I feel good for a moment for being the "best," I feel guilty for making you feel bad about yourself. I set this standard for perfectionism to better myself, but now I am judgmental of myself and others for not being good enough, so I do not deserve love."

Activity 3.5
Exploring Perfectionism
Think of a time when you desired perfectionism as a defense for feelings of inadequacy or low self-esteem. Describe your thoughts, actions, and feelings. Explore how you feel when you strain to achieve perfection.

Ways you strain for perfectionism:

_____

_____

_____

_____

How does your perfectionism make you feel?
About yourself:

_____

_____

About others:

_____

_____

***

Angry Dependency

Angry dependency (LO, pp. 58, 131, 152) occurs when people become excessively dependent on others to fulfill their needs. When the dependent person's needs are not met, they become angry. Angry dependency can develop when a child grows up with neglectful or rejecting parents. This feeling of being rejected by their parent causes children pain. When this pain becomes distinct, the child may call out or act up and demand that their needs be met. Children do this early on in life with parents and other caregiver authorities and continue to do this later in life with other interpersonal relationships as well. After lacking gratification from their parents early on in life, children may grow up with the feeling that they always need fulfillment of needs for caring, esteem, and narcissistic valuing to make up for what they missed from their parents. For example, if a child is never told he or she is loved by the parent and never feels wanted, the child will struggle to fill needs such as caring and esteem as they grow older. They then become excessively dependent on other people to make up for their unmet needs. This also leaves little room in the personality for independence.

The ongoing desire for these needs to be fulfilled by others becomes unhealthy by crippling needs for independence, autonomy and self-agency. Furthermore, by depending on others to fulfill certain needs, anger continues to grow as insatiable demands get frustrated. Angry dependency can be put into words, as in stating to someone, "I have never felt loved and cared for before and I really want to feel these things. Do you know how much pain I suffered by being rejected as a child? To avoid this pain, I am depending on you to fulfill my needs for me. When you do not fulfill my needs, I get very angry with you because you are not being the good mother I need to soothe my pains."

Activity 3.6
Finding Consequences of Angry Dependency
Relax and think of a time when you were angry and dependent or are angry and dependent on others as a defense mechanism. Describe your thoughts, actions, and feelings. Also, what problems do you think the anger and dependency create rather than solve?

Angry Dependency: _____

_____

_____

Problems angry dependency causes:

_____

_____

_____

***

Entitlement
Entitlement (LO, pp. 58, 73-74, 109)—a close kin to angry dependency—is the belief that you have a right to something. Entitlement is an extension of childhood omnipotence that arises when an infant or toddler experiences either neglect of its own needs or overindulgence from its parents. When this happens, the child may become fixated on or stuck in a childish position of expecting and demanding that others always be the good parent that they never had. In the same way that a mother makes sure an infant's life is comfortable and easy, an individual with entitlement will expect that the world and everyone in it act in this "good motherly" way to make sure their life is comfortable and easy. When others do not provide us with the things we feel entitled to, we become angry at life and everyone in it. We are angry that life is not full of the endless comfort and good fortune that we feel entitled to.

Think back to the example of the person who missed out on his need for attention and love from his parents. Because his parent did not meet these needs when he was a child, as he grows into adulthood, he will stay fixated on having his early needs fulfilled. He will then expect that everyone around him fulfill his needs by giving him all the attention, support and love that he desires, even if it is childlike at this point. He will feel entitled to these needs since they were not previously met and he had spent his childhood longing for them. Putting entitlement into words is like saying to someone, "My needs were not met when I was a child. Because I had so much hurt and pain from this, I am now entitled to it. I deserve this no matter what, and if you do not give me what I deserve I will be mad and punish you."

Activity 3.7
Elaborating Entitlement

Relax, breathe in and out on your 5 counts for several beats. Be still, then think of a time when you felt entitled to something because you did not receive it when you were a child. Describe your thoughts, actions, and feelings in words.

Write down what you want in the moment:

_____

_____

_____

_____

_____

_____

Entitlement feelings: Express how you feel that getting what you want makes up for past childhood hurts.

_____

_____

_____

_____

_____

Cruelty
There are many negative defense mechanisms and character faults that can come from childhood developmental issues or trauma. Any feeling or state can act as a defense mechanism for another state by warding off or repressing deeper feelings, longing, and needs. On the deepest level, chronic negative feelings defend against love, surrender, and

peace, fearing that these positive states and affects are heralds of danger because of our history of trauma, psychic injury, and developmental troubles. For instance, hate can defend against surrender to love as it becomes a racket to keep us from feeling deep hurt, longing, and fear of surrender to another person. Hate and fear can also become a way to defend against a deep sense of peace if we hold on to them to prevent the danger of peace being a "false prophet" and therefore entrapment and abuse.

The anger and aggression that we have from childhood rarely remains just anger and aggression. Overall, it is evident that when our natural tendency for love and closeness is not satisfied, we experience negative feelings and wishes. These negative feelings and wishes stem from our love that is "outraged." It can be said that these character faults culminate in cruelty, which is just the final stage of the hurt and pain we feel when our need for love is not fulfilled. The cruelty in these defenses is comparable to saying to someone, "I am going to be cruel to you, to get pleasure out of causing you pain. If I can get pleasure out of your pain, then I will know that I do not need love or anything like it."

Outright cruelty that accrues from love outraged is the cause of the deepest shame in our personality, but it is common. Some of us have only the slightest touch of meanness, and some have to the point that it seems unbearable. If it becomes absolutely unbearable, the guilt and shame for the cruelty is repressed. When this happens, the cruel person forecloses the pain of guilt and pretends he or she doesn't feel anything for other people. This is the development of the anti-social personality. Help for this type of problem comes by connecting the past hurts and shame with the current character fault of cruelty and by helping the individual accept the pain of their repressed or denied guilt.

Fortunately, most of us only have cruel impulses in small measure that cause us guilt and shame. In this case, the guilt and pain for our cruelty keeps us connected to our higher self. This level of cruelty is often thought of as a mean streak in an otherwise healthy personality.

Getting in touch with the darkest element of our lower self, our cruelty, is the greatest step in self-awareness, and accepting it and detoxifying cruelty is the greatest step in our growth upward into our higher, greater self. This being said, it is important to remember that cruelty and all lower self traits and problems are defenses against the best and greatest in all of us. Love, joy, and altruism cause fear in an immature personality.

Activity 3.8
Daily Review
Try, over the period of a few weeks, to keep a journal of daily troubles in your life. In your daily review, describe in the following chart a time when over a few weeks you experienced each of these negative faults. Then fill in the rest of the squares by responding to the prompts at the left of each row (*see chart on the next page*).

Lower Self as Child Within
Many of the character faults t described above can be seen as childish traits. Children, in addition to being wonderful, loving little beings, are often envious, contemptuous, exhibit angry dependency, and feel entitled, among many other troubles. The 18th century philosopher Jean Jacques Rousseau called children "noble tyrants."

Our lower selves resemble and are composed of childlike attitudes and demands. Our lower selves have many of the same ignorant beliefs that children have. It is normal for children to have these negative traits and ignorant beliefs. However, as we grow older, we are supposed to grow out of these things. When we do not grow out of these negative traits, they reside in our lower self; therefore, in a sense the lower self can be viewed as a wounded and troubled child within us.

Those of us who have a strong, troubled child within have had love outraged through hurt, pain, and trauma. This pain causes dysphoric feelings and attributes that need to be processed before they become more aggressive. Because the negative feelings and beliefs of the child within have resided in the lower self for so long and have caused so much pain, they are hard to reach and process. Nevertheless, the depth psychological approach can reach this level of the personality, bring it to the surface, and into play in treatment. When these elements are faced with courage and dedication, they can be transformed over time. Through this transformation, we can break free from their grasp and mature to a great degree into truly loving individuals.

On the next page is a grid that may be used to help you understand and transform your faults.

Character Faults	Envy	Spite	Contempt	Perfectionism	Angry Dependency	Entitlement
When did you confront this fault?						
How did you feel before and after you acted out this fault?						
Did you think this will soothe your pain forever?						
From what psychic injury did your fault truly stem from?						
What is your fault protecting you from?						
What can you do differently now?						

***

We are all children at one time. Therefore, at one point we have all possessed these childlike needs, attitudes, and irrational beliefs. We all have some troubles and negative elements that we should transcend or grow out of. Transcendence of these negative traits is possible depending on the severity of the hurt and the resources available. However, at times the hurt, trauma, and troubles are too great, and the environment does not provide the necessary resources to facilitate health and maturity. When a child endures this type of experience, their pain and aggression become immense and unmanageable, often ending in character faults, troublesome feelings, and needs, and sometimes severe mental illness. The child within who endured this pain and injury does not go away but becomes what we refer to as the lower self. When we become an adult, the lower self or the child within must be embraced and held in therapy by a caring and present therapist. Through the depth psychological approach and emotional embrace by a caring and present therapist or helper of some kind, the lower self-elements can emerge and become available for transformation.

The Ego
Since Freudian psychology has worked its way into our everyday life, the reader may already be implicitly aware of many of his ideas. To help the reader make these basic ideas clearer, a brief explanation of some basic elements of Freudian psychology is helpful. Sigmund Freud, the founding father of depth psychology, originally used the term "I" to represent the sense of oneself that is conscious and knowable. Elements that we are not conscious of and are out of our awareness were referred to as the "It" (LO, pp. 45-46, 48). Freud used the term "Over I" to describe the part of our minds that evaluates us morally. Eventually, in the English language, the "I" became the ego, the "It" became the id, and the "Over I" became the superego. To prevent confusion, from now on we will use the terms ego, id, and superego.

The id represents our internal drives, feelings, and instincts without any connection to the external world. The id operates on the pleasure principle, which is the idea that every wish and desire should be satisfied regardless of the consequences. The id also engages in primary process thinking, a form of irrational, spontaneous thinking. Overall, the id is the part of our minds that acts impulsively to fulfill our desire for pleasure and happiness regardless of external elements. When we are born, the id is the only part of our minds that is used; we operate solely on our instincts, drives, and impulses. The following examples of infants and toddlers illustrate how we act when only using the id. The moment a child is hungry, he cries until he is fed; when he wants a toy that another child is already using, he does not hesitate to take the toy out of the other child's hand. These behaviors eventually decrease as we grow older; this is because we start to develop and utilize the ego.

The ego has many functions such as judgment, discrimination, adapting to reality, synthesizing internal drives and feelings with external reality, and tolerating feelings and frustration. In a sense, the ego can be viewed as the opposite of the id. The ego operates according to the reality principle—considering the external world—and uses rational, realistic thinking. The ego plays a mediating role between the id and external reality by trying to compromise the desires of the id while also coping with and adapting to external reality. Keeping in mind the previous examples, notice how the behaviors of the character's change as they become adults who have developed their ego. When sitting in class, a child becomes hungry and wants to eat immediately; however, knowing that he has an exam coming up, he waits until class is over to satisfy his need for food. A teenager may want to use his brother's car; however, knowing that his brother would be mad if he took it without asking, he instead asks if he may borrow the car. The ego wants the same things that the id wants—food and objects—but the ego develops a realistic strategy to obtain these things.

From a spiritual point of view, the ego can be looked at a little differently, as an extension of our involuntary feeling self. The ego develops as life frustrations and hurdles cause us to need to delay our wishes and think of new ways to achieve what we desire. Freud believed that logic and reason, and their ability to manage impulses, were the only elements that could save humanity. From a spiritual perspective, we do have instincts and we need to control these instincts; however, there is an alternative to ego control and mastery that is more expansive, liberating, and peace inducing. This alternative is more important than intellectual or willful ego control and more intuitive and wiser than ego logic.

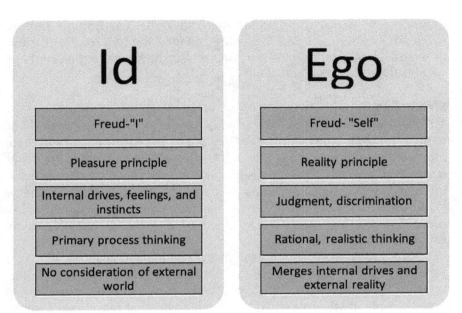

Figure 2
Spiritual Point of View of Ego

This alternative is a place where the ego seeks guidance from our inner wisdom, which is connected to our life stream—the greater self of life and the involuntary—of love. The ego is not abandoned; rather, it becomes subordinate to the life lived from passionate wisdom and the creative, intuitive core self within. Furthermore, although the ego is essential, our core self and the life stream within is more important. Consider logic, reason, and intuition; logic and reason are important functions of the mind but are subordinate to intuition. In the same way, if life is to be spontaneous and meaningful, then a strong ego is needed—not as a final measure of development but so that it can surrender to the greater core self of life and the involuntary.

Weak Ego
When the ego is too weak, our feelings and impulses override our control and balance so that we are not in command of our own ship. Weak ego (LO, pp. 49) formation may result in drug or alcohol addiction or other addictions such as gambling or compulsive spending. People are often driven by their impulses and feel out of control. They lack the capacity to delay gratification of needs and have poor self-soothing. When they are denied gratification, they have difficulty distracting

themselves with nurturing replacement strategies like finding comfort in friends, positive self -talk, believing and focusing on a positive future, or even feeling gratitude for the good things they have in that moment of their lives.

Strong Ego

The ego must be able to contain these real feelings and examine them to discover their true meaning so they can be transformed back to their more loving state. A strong ego (LO, pp. 49) is both able to delay frustration of needs and feelings and at the same time be aware of most impulses and feelings. A strong ego accepts that one may be angry, jealous, envious, ungrateful, or even feel mean but consciously contains these feelings and deals with them by moderated expression or renunciation.

Moderated expression means that if you have a mean impulse you recognize it but try to choose an assertive manner of expression instead. For example, if I am really mad at a friend because he has criticized me, instead of criticizing back or putting him down I might say, "Ouch; it hurts when you say that, and I think you are being rude."

An example of renunciation might be if a friend has a sudden inheritance that makes me envious and creates a feeling of wanting to spoil his good fortune but, instead, I say to myself, "This is a human feeling; you are jealous, but he is your friend. Do not make him feel bad or try to discount his success."

For this to happen, the ego must be strong and resilient enough to accomplish four things: (1) accept unflattering desires and experiences into awareness, (2) undo repression, (3) allow for mourning, and (4) allow for transformation.

Activity 3.9
Developing a Strong and Resilient Ego by Observation and Affirmation

Breathe in and out for your 5 counts several times. Be still. Listen for any unflattering, unacceptable, or negative feelings that might emerge that you usually turn away from. Let them float in your mind and be present there for a while.

Try to accept them with the affirmation that these are part of me but do not define me.

Feel the pain of the unflattering negative thoughts you are feeling. Stay with the pain a while.

Talk to the wounded child within about the negative thoughts and feelings.

As you observe these feelings, acknowledge you are okay that you have them, knowing they don't define you; you are more than these feelings.

Let them go to the ether, as you breathe out.

Affirm you are the good, loving person who is observing these thoughts and are in the process of moving on from them.

***

Rigid Ego

Along with being strong, an ego must be flexible rather than rigid. An ego is rigid (LO, pp. 50) when it is over controlled, causing it to use too much repression in defending against unconscious negativity. This over-control can cause anxiety, other neurotic symptoms, and many other problems. Having a rigid ego can also cause individuals to use compulsions and addictions as a release from this over-controlled ego. Conversely, a strong and flexible ego can contain negative feelings in consciousness and transform them by understanding their source as love outraged at the core.

When the ego self is rigid with strict rational decision making, our conscious self and our death anxiety (LO, pp. 15, 18, 51) increases. It increases because our administrative faculties are the only thing considered, not our intuitive self that is connected to the life stream. The unconscious processes are increasingly feared not only because they are negative but also because the ego becomes so narrow that the core self is not identified with; rather, it represents non-being or death. When the ego is flexible, the feeling self and the life stream are identified with, death becomes safer, and anxiety diminishes. This state can be achieved through meditation and breathing exercises. The problem with this transcendental type of meditation is that the already positive, strengthened aspects of the personality are benefited but the negative, destructive aspects remain the same.

Ego Omnipotence

The ego can also be released by surrendering our sense of omnipotence—the inner psychological belief that we should oversee all that is around us. Although we are not in charge of everything that is around us, we engage is something called *the need for rulership.* The need for rulership is when we force everything to fit our wants and needs, including our desire to force others to love us and put us first. We unconsciously try to force all aspects of life to fit our needs rather than accepting the realities of life. Have you ever heard the expression, "the world does not revolve around you"? Those who have not surrendered their ego omnipotence (LO, pp. 51) believe and act as if the world does revolve around them. They try to force life to fit their many fantasized wishes and outrageous needs (i.e., being the center of attention, always first, always best, and always loved), creating tension and forcing others to act a certain way. Ignoring reality and trying to force everything around us to be as we want it to be is the opposite of letting go into the life stream. In contrast, the accepting state goes into the life stream with the belief that whatever life hands us we can handle with trust and patient understanding.

People living from an ego-omnipotent state of being are often angry at all the little things in life. They are mad that they have to work, mad that they have to pay bills, mad that money doesn't magically fall in their lap, mad that the day only has 24 hours, mad when there is too much noise, mad that the weather is too cold, mad when they are confronted and when they may be wrong, mad when they are lonely, and mad when too many people are around. They are sometimes even mad that they have to take care of their personal hygiene such as brushing their teeth. They are the people who want to be great singers but don't want to have to take singing lessons, or wonderful dancers but without taking dancing lessons, or doctors and lawyers although they don't want to have to go to college.

The accepting state does not try to force anything, such as love, and is only reached when you can let others and life be without trying to coerce it to align with your fantasies. Engaging in meditation and introspection daily allows individuals to work toward moving from a state of omnipotence to acceptance. Through meditation and introspection, we can try to understand how and why we get upset when others reject us, criticize us, or do not behave in a way that we believe will calm our self-doubts.

When we do not get what we want from others—such as being told how good we are or how much we are loved—we become angry. These or any other omnipotent demand should be acknowledged and accepted. Acceptance doesn't mean resignation. It means accepting this state as our temporary reality until we can change it.

When this anger occurs, the best thing to do is to breathe into it and acknowledge it; through acknowledging it we experience the pain of not getting what we wanted. After this pain is experienced, see if you can sit with the pain for a moment. If you can do that, one day you will be able to tolerate it for a longer period and then your tolerance and surrender to life grows. The journey to the accepting state can be broken down into five stages (see Figure 3): experiencing anxiety and anger, acknowledging our feelings, allowing the experience, augmenting tolerance, and reaching acceptance.

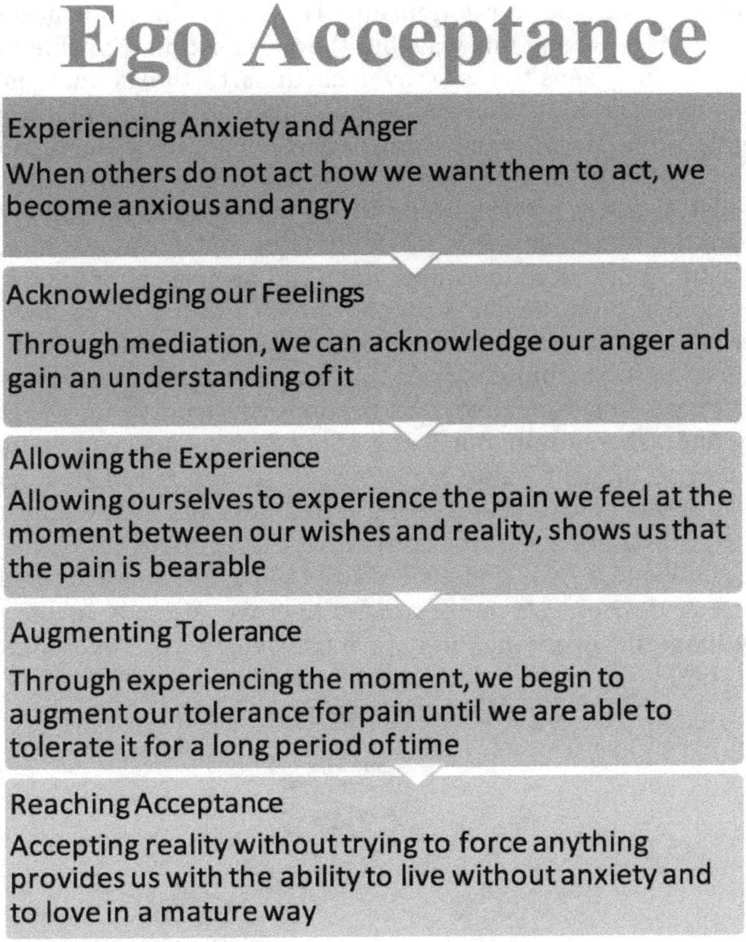

Ego Acceptance

Experiencing Anxiety and Anger

When others do not act how we want them to act, we become anxious and angry

Acknowledging our Feelings

Through mediation, we can acknowledge our anger and gain an understanding of it

Allowing the Experience

Allowing ourselves to experience the pain we feel at the moment between our wishes and reality, shows us that the pain is bearable

Augmenting Tolerance

Through experiencing the moment, we begin to augment our tolerance for pain until we are able to tolerate it for a long period of time

Reaching Acceptance

Accepting reality without trying to force anything provides us with the ability to live without anxiety and to love in a mature way

Figure 3

When ego omnipotence is high, it is considered the childlike state of omnipotence. In this childlike state, time is not recognized as temporary, meaning that whatever feeling is occurring now is going to last forever. This state does not realize that when you experience hurt you may forget about it within a matter of minutes. One of the best ways to cope with this childlike state of omnipotence is to deal with it as transference in psychotherapy. Transference in psychotherapy entails the client acting in therapy the same way they do in all other aspects of their life. Their omnipotence and attempts to force life to fit the desires of their ego identity and self-will are also seen in the therapeutic setting and in the therapeutic relationship. The client does not necessarily know that he is acting this way, but the therapist may be able to point out the client's sensitivity or overreactions to things such as being slightly late for a session or being distracted. If the therapist can recognize the client's ego omnipotence, they can work together to develop patience and recognize how often the client expects the therapist to act in accordance with the client's demands. For this to happen, the therapist needs to kindly point out these instances over time to bring the client to awareness. If this awareness of omnipotence never occurs, then the client will not be able to live an accepting life, and eventually more malicious emotions will accrue such as hate.

Pushing for omnipotence causes a vicious cycle (see Figure 4) of guilt, shame, anger, anxiety, and keeping you from loving. If you are guilty and ashamed for not being able to love, then you want more reassurance of your value from others, so you begin to force this. Forcing others to love us and trying to fit others and their emotions into our fantasies is not a mature state of love. To get out of our bondage, we must allow and accept that others and their emotions will not always fulfill our desires. We must accept that we are not in control of everything and everyone, and we must believe that everything will work out.

Ego Omnipotence Cycle

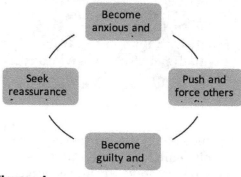

Figure 4

False Self
The false self or mask (LO, pp. 53-54, 59, 132, 134, 156, 166) is the aspect of our personality that acts in whichever way it believes the external world wants us to. The false self can be viewed as a mask that we wear to please others. The false self shrouds the lower self to sublimate, dissociate, and repress internal impulses. By not acting solely on impulses and wearing a mask, we are less likely to receive retribution, criticism, and rejection from others. The false self also shrouds the core so that our true self is not shown to others and the external world; rather, it is covered up by a mask of what and how we want others to see us.

The false self has good intentions of gaining the most concern, esteem, love, and safety it can from others. It is designed to read the environment and can predict the best and most acceptable way of being, according to the external world. Nevertheless, the false self's impulses of wanting to make others happy also threatens one's overall sense of well-being. It puts so much attention and energy into pleasing others that it does not have any concern for pleasing the self. Spontaneous impulses, needs, and feelings are completely ignored leaving us a life without zest and passion.

The false self is developed early in life because of parental commands and expectations. Parents often create a firm template and boundaries around their children. This is because the value of appearing good to others is viewed as more important than children's inner subjective experience of themselves and who they are. Think back to your childhood. Are there things that your parents forbade you to recognize in yourself such as unhappiness or angry feelings or beliefs that seemed forced or foreign to your inner spirit? For example, maybe they pushed you to play sports, so you are now an athlete, and everyone views you this way. However, you never liked sports much, and found more enjoyment from music. Your interest in music is part of your core self, and your interest in sports is part of your false-self mask. Some children may be raised with the belief that men are supposed to have a career and the woman is supposed to stay home with the children. Young men may present themselves to others as career oriented; however, what they may truly desire is to stay home with their children.

You may have grown up with the idea that you have to be a nice guy. Jealousy, resentment, aggressiveness as means to get ahead may have been considered bad and you were supposed to replace these feelings with kindness and accepting second place or less. You grow up with a mask of kindness that hides your competitiveness, ambition, aggression. You become passive and timid. You wonder why you always feel unhappy, depressed and life doesn't work for you. You are guilty when you are assertive and fearful if you want to be the best. You hide behind the image of second-place "nice guy," and your resentments grow, as does your lower self. You become mad at life for being left behind and because you are the proverbial doormat.

The way out is to realize you are hiding your aggression, your competitiveness for the sake of being the "nice guy." You need to realize the cost of this mask and how it keeps you perpetually depressed and self-depreciating. Only then can you become assertive, take on the game of life, and fight for a good and successful place in it.

There are many masks or false selves: the hero, the tough guy, the sultry diva, the perfect gentleman, the boss. Whatever role you take on that forecloses a free expression of multiple elements of your personality may be a false self or mask. The tough guy hides vulnerability, the sultry diva may hide dependency, and the hero may hide his fear.

Who one is and one's spontaneity, passion, and zest for life cannot be liberated until the mask of the false self is deconstructed. It is important to know that the false self, the ego, and the lower self need to be embraced, accepted, and integrated into the core self. These parts of the personality, which are defensive and conflicted, should never be criticized or torn down to hopeless states. Furthermore, the more these elements of the self are embraced and seen as a transitional phenomenon, the more they can be transformed. Transformation of these elements requires a lot of patience and faith in the depth analytic attitude, negative capability, and negative containment. Pushing and criticizing the lower elements will only cause them to become repressed again without any healing or transformation taking place. Get to them, accept them, mourn the pain that caused them, and find the higher self-elements or real caring loving elements behind the negative or false elements of the personality. This is the project of *Love Outraged and the Liberation of the Core Self.*

Lower Self
As mentioned earlier, the lower self is our dark side or shadow (LO, pp. 6, 33-34, 45-46, 50, 56, 102,107, 13,126,164,167,172). It consists of our faults or desire for separateness, our belief that we are constantly at war with others and have to defeat them or we will be defeated. It is also the place in us, as Rumi that great Sufi poet would say, that takes pleasure in others' misfortune. It is based in our trauma developmental

troubles and has the negative trinity of faults: hubristic pride, self-will or a forcing current toward others and life, and ultimately fear. Do remember that the lower self also contains much of your passion and zest for life although it is distorted into negativity. By owning, containing it in conscious awareness, and journeying to transform it, you begin to liberate the passion it contains.

Activity 3.10
Draw Your Lower Self as a Face

Using all you have learned about yourself thus far, muster your courage to make a list and add labels that illustrate many of your faults and negative feelings. Keep in mind that you are doing this to start your journey upward and inward to transform these faults into higher self qualities.

Lower Self

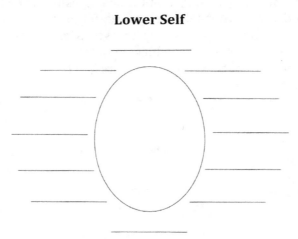

Idealized Self
The idealized self (LO, pp. 59, 82) uses defenses that we are not always aware of, such as unrealistically striving to be perfect and exaggerating self-worth and power. These defenses are attempts to deny vulnerability, shame, anxiety, and other dysphoric feelings. Overall, the idealized self can be viewed as something that is destructive and defensive. Unlike the lower self, the idealized self is an image of a perfect self that one strives to be, and it tyrannizes us with "shoulds" and unrealistic expectations. It does not accept less than perfection and we can never be perfect.

Think of the word "ideal" in idealized. Your ideal self would be perfect. However, this ideal self and idea of perfectionism are not realistic. Furthermore, it would be ideal never to be late for anything throughout your entire life; however, is that realistic? Probably not, You are more than likely going to be late at least once. Holding ourselves to the standard that we will always be on time, and we will be perfect is setting ourselves up for failure. These unhealthy needs do not provide us with emotional growth, physical health, or healthy emotional mutuality in relationships.

Activity 3.11
False Self–Mask

Take a moment and think about how you present yourself to others. How do others see you? What do others think about you? What do others know about you? Using the face below, draw a mask of how others view you. For example, do they see you smiling or frowning? In addition to drawing your false-self mask, fill in the surrounding lines with words or phrases that describe how you present yourself to others (e.g., serious, caring, energetic, selfless, quiet, a person who likes sports, someone who does not enjoy the outdoors, etc.).

***

False Self

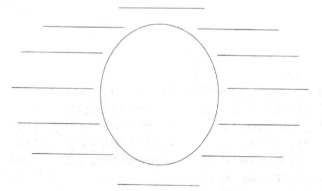

Total Self

Adding another dimension to our personality theory, we will call this your total self. The total self is you as you really feel, with your highs and your lows, your faults and virtues as you make your way through the world. Sometimes you might be proud of your total self; sometimes maybe not because it is not always the nicest part of you.

Activity 3.12
Accepting your Total, Real Self

For the next part of this activity, draw yourself as if you were not wearing a mask—perhaps as you really feel most often or right now. Come as close as you can get to your highs and lows without pretense, free of having to make an impression on others or even yourself. For example, maybe your false-self mask showed you happy and gleaming with confidence, but underneath the mask you are sad and scared. If you are having a hard time with this, try to think of how you are when no one is around. After you complete the drawing, continue filling in the lines around the face with words or phrases that describe who you are without a mask on. These are things that others may not see or know about you. They are characteristics that others would not attribute to you but you would. For example, maybe you wrote "reserved" as a personality trait for your false self because this is how people view you; however, you really view yourself as someone who is outgoing and adventurous.

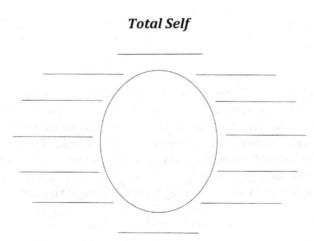

Total Self

Activity 3.13
Drawing Your Core Self

Draw yourself presenting the best in you. It may even resemble the false self, but it is not necessarily what you present to the world. It is the best in you when you are sitting alone and quiet and which others don't even see. This is the self where you feel safe and can afford to love and give your best. It is also the seat of your creativity, intuition, and inspiration. Sometimes the false-self pretense of being always nice and loving charades as a core-self element. The core self is loving, of course, but it has a different feel. It is not ingratiatingly sweet or passive; it feels genuine, real, and inspirational. Sometimes we pretend to feel loving even when we are critical or judgmental, which is the false self.

Core Self

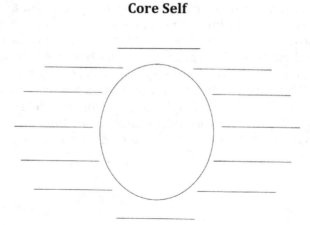

Activity 3.14
Distinguishing the Core Self from the False-Self Mask

Compare the false-self activity to the core elements. Explore the differences between your false self—when you are wearing a mask, and your core self—when you are not wearing a mask. If you do not see a lot of differences between the two faces, spend some time thinking about the following questions, and complete your core- and false-self drawings again before continuing with the rest of the activity.

Questions to better evaluate and describe the false self and core self.

- If you were to ask someone else to complete the false-self face for you, would it still look the same?
- Are there things that you enjoy that others do not know about?
- Do you like and enjoy every aspect of your false-self mask?
- Did someone tell you or teach you to present yourself in a certain way? Have you always wanted to present yourself in that way?
- Did you make sure that your false-self mask consists only of things that make others happy?
- Does your core self consist only of things that make you happy?

Once there are noticeable differences between your two faces, explore the following questions. This is not meant to be done quickly; these are questions that you can answer now or think thoroughly about before answering. Also, there is never a right or wrong answer, and you can have more than one answer to each question.

- Was the false-self or core-self faces easier for you to complete? Why do you think this is?
- When did you develop the aspects of your false-self mask?
- Who influenced your false-self mask (e.g., family, society, beliefs)?
- Does it feel different imagining living more from your real self with its faults and foibles then it does from your mask?
- Are there aspects of your false-self mask that you dislike more than others? Why?
- Do the elements of your false-self mask that you especially dislike have anything in common (e.g., influenced by the same person, developed at the same time, seen only in certain settings)?
- Do you wear your false-self mask to make others happy or yourself?
- Is there any part of your false-self mask that you wish was part of your core self?
- Do you have more than one false-self mask depending on your surroundings and situation? How might your false-self mask be different in different situations?

- Do you have your false-self mask on always, even when you are alone?
- Is there a time other than when you are alone that you are not wearing your false-self mask?
- Are their times you live from your real self? How does this feel compared to living from your mask?
- Are there positive aspects of your false self that can be embraced?
- How can you work toward deconstructing your false-self mask so that only your core self is utilized?
- Examine your lower self's faults. Do you see the higher-self distortions in them such as envy being the distortion of admiration, hostility the distortion of positive boundaries or longing for love and its derivatives outraged. Try to find these in every fault. We are all good and loving at our core.

***

Other Important Personality Elements

Subjectivity

It is very important to understand psychological subjectivity as an element in the liberation process. Psychological subjectivity (LO, pp. 60) can be viewed as individualism or uniqueness. Each child is unique in their own way; no two children are the same. We all have our own individual elements that make up our personality—our own needs, wishes, desires, dreams, ideas, and self-direction, which we call our subjectivity. When a child's subjectivity is not embraced, honored, and encouraged, the child disowns him- or herself. In other words, when a parent does not accept a child for who he or she is, the child begins to believe that they cannot and should not be themselves, so they attempt to get rid of their subjectivity—their unique elements.

Activity 3.15
Explore Your Own Psychological Subjectivity - Part 1

Name some ways that made you unique from your parents, siblings, or other children. Fill in the lines below that apply to you and your psychological subjectivity.

What made me happy as a child _____

What I desired as a child _____

What I needed as a child _____

My dream as a child _____

As a child, I was _____

As a child, I valued _____

As a child, I believed _____

A child's subjectivity can be damaged through parents' expectations, regardless of how subtle they are. When a parent expects a child to be the parent's version of "good" without consideration of the child's subjectivity, violence is done to the child. When parents have expectations that their child should not be unhappy, should not complain, should only desire what the parent wants, and should always adopt the parents' values and beliefs, violence is done to the child's inner subjectivity and core self.

***

Activity 3.15
Explore your Parent's Expectations and Template They Had for You - Part 2

Name some ways your parents were different from your psychological subjectivity, which you explored above.

My parents expected my happiness to come from:

_____

My parents wanted me to desire:

_____

My parents thought I needed:

_____

My parents dream for me was:

_____

My parents believed I should have always been:

_____

My parents wanted me to value:

_____

My parents wanted me to believe:

_____

Parents should guide, encourage, and have expectations for their children. However, this becomes problematic when parents overtly or covertly force their own template on how their child should be and do not understand the child's subjective needs, wishes, fears, and longings. Parents should develop an understanding of their child's subjectivity; rather than insisting their child disown or betray him- or herself, they should guide, encourage, and point out consequences to their child. Parents should take a subjectivity-embracing position with their children. This position requires parents to understand children's dysphoric complaints and feelings rather than punishing their children for having them. This position does not discourage children from having wishes and desires; rather, it helps shape these wishes and desires, along with the child's readiness to grow and develop.

Children who are discouraged from valuing their inner subjectivity turn away from themselves and what they want. They begin to base their desires and values entirely on what their parents want and, eventually, by way of transference, on what other authority figures want. This then causes individuals to forsake the self and identify with others to determine what is good, valuable, and right in life. In other words, individuals no longer base what they want in their life on themselves; they base it on what others want. When people lack self-identification, they struggle to make any decisions on their own. They must run ideas, opinions, and wants through others before making any final decisions. In the rare case these individuals do make a decision on their own without getting prior approval, they experience great anxiety.

The lack of self-identification is crippling to an individual in many ways. These individuals are always looking for directions, or ways to know what is good and right. These directions may be found in a book, such as relying on a Bible to tell them what is right or wrong. These directions may not always be literal; they can also involve another person's facial expressions or actions, such as waiting for a nod of approval from someone. Individuals without self-identification must seek out and receive approval for their thoughts, feelings, and actions; otherwise they perceive danger is eminent.

***

Activity 3.15
Exploring the Difference between Parents Forcing an Iron Template or Embracing the Child's Subjectivity – Part 3

This exercise is designed to help you see the different outcomes that can occur when parents take either a subjectivity-embracing position or a subjectivity-denying position Now that you have explored both your own subjectivity and your parents' expectations of you, compare them to each another. Do most of the ways you listed in Parts 1 and 2 match up, or are most them different? List some of the ways your subjectivity was inconsistent with your parents' expectations of you. Then spend some time exploring how these areas affected you in childhood and how they currently affect you. Read the following examples before completing the activity for yourself.

Subjectivity-Embracing Example:

One way my subjectivity was inconsistent with my parents' expectations was that I wanted to be an artist, but they wanted me to be a doctor.

My childhood was affected because I grew up knowing that although I did not have the same dream as my parents, they still supported me. They encouraged me to get a college education even though I did not want to.

I am currently affected because their encouragement to get a college degree has provided me with opportunities as an artist that would not have been available if I had not gone to college. I now know what I want in life and go after it, but I also accept advice from others.

Template-Forcing Example:

One way my subjectivity aligned with my parent's expectations was that I needed love and compassion from them, but they thought structure and discipline were more important.

My childhood was affected because I grew up thinking that I was not lovable and that it was not okay for me to desire affection or show affection to others.

I am currently affected because I am constantly questioning how I should feel and if it is okay to express my feelings. I always base my feelings on what other people are feeling or on how they tell me I should feel. This has caused me to struggle in making and maintaining many of my relationships.

One way my subjectivity was inconsistent with my parent's expectations:

_____

_____

_____

My childhood was affected:

_____

_____

_____

I am currently affected:

_____

_____

_____

One way my subjectivity was inconsistent with my parent's expectations:

_____

_____

_____

My childhood was affected:

_____

_____

_____

I am currently affected:

_____

_____

_____

One way my subjectivity was inconsistent with my parent's expectations:

_____

_____

_____

My childhood was affected:

_____

_____

_____

I am currently affected:

_____

_____

_____

***

People who have had their soul, inner subjectivity, and self-identification squeezed out of them in this way have much work to do. Individuals who have forsaken their own subjectivity must spend a great deal of time examining their reactions to others and try to discern whether they function from secondary reactions or always need to read others before they make decisions or let themselves want or need something. Try not to kid yourself. If you basically disqualify yourself and look to friends, loved ones, or authorities outside of yourself to form your opinions or decide whether it is okay to want something or speak your mind, you have a lack of self-identification.

If you discover this lack in yourself, to whatever degree and in each particular way that it occurs, you will notice that you wait, listen and examine others for validation before you make a decision or an expression of need or something you value. This is a secondary reaction—secondary because it is not yours originally but comes through your reading of others before you act. Instead of basing your actions opinions or need on these secondary reactions, pause and note what you are doing. Then breathe for a minute and tune into yourself. Ask yourself if this your real opinion, feeling, or need or rather something you borrowed. Try to feel into your gut and soul what you really want, even if you are afraid to think of it or long for it. Then note your primary reaction.

You don't even have to speak your primary, authentic reaction at first or act on it. Just note it. If you feel you have to speak it or act on your primary reaction, you may foreclose recognition of it for fear that it will cause rejection from those around you. At first just note that your primary reaction is different than your secondary reaction. After you practice this for a while, you will begin to tune into yourself more and identify with yourself, your needs, your wants and wishes—in other words your own subjectivity. This will help free you from your dependency on others for approval and foster a belief in yourself and self-validation you have not known before, which will help liberate your core self-longings.

Sometimes achieving self-identification is very hard to do alone, and we seek psychotherapy for help. In treatment, through therapeutic presence, empathy, and encouragement for self-validation, people begin to believe in themselves again over time and redevelop their sense of self-identification. It can be necessary for the therapist to encourage the individual to question the therapist's opinion or point of view. This can help the individual decide for themselves whether they agree with the therapist's opinion or not. They begin to recognize their primary reactions and not just their secondary ones. This develops a belief that the individual's own opinion and needs do matter and that they have a valid position in any relationships.

It is essential for therapists to help clients realize they do have an important, valid position in the therapeutic relationship. They often believe that if they think or do something it is wrong, or if their friend doubts them or does not like what they want, that their opinion is automatically invalid. The same way they behave in their relationships outside of psychotherapy, they will also behave inside the therapeutic relationship. When this transference occurs, it is important to gently point out to the client what is happening. For example, a therapist might tell a client, "I notice you are trying to read me and figure out what I want. I believe in you. What do you feel and think?" For a client to gain their self-identification, they must first be encouraged not to automatically assume that they are wrong in the therapeutic relationship. They must be encouraged to pause and tune into their own thoughts, feelings, and desires to gain a sense of what they think is right or good. When they can tune in to what they believe, they must be able to stand behind their beliefs enough to communicate their position.

Will

Will (LO, pp. 62) is the impulse to self-direct, to affect our world, and create ourselves. In other words, will is our impulse to act on our personal desires, which affect both our external world and our internal self—who we are. Having this will and impulse to separate and individuate always comes with anxiety because it causes fear of loss and abandonment. Will has two polarities of existence: the desire to unite and be at one with others, especially the mother, and the desire to create one's own self and life. On one hand, our will strives to be connected to people and to feel a sense of belonging. On the other hand, our will strives to be unique, individual, separate, and distinct from others.

Along with fear and anxiety, this will contains a moral component that experiences guilt as we individuate. The guilt stems from our empathy and concern for others, which we acquire at birth through attachment. As we begin to individuate, we develop a sense of guilt for leaving behind previous attachments that we had with others. We fear that as we leave behind the people and previous relationships we had that they will be hurt and damaged. Our will is the part of our ego that takes the universal desire for attachment and belongingness and drives us toward becoming separate and unique individuals.

In childhood, will is expressed as counterwill (LO, pp. 73-74). A great example of a child expressing counterwill is when a two-year old's favorite word becomes "no." This is the child's way of beginning to define herself and forge an independent identity. As frustrating as it can be when a two-year old responds with "no" to everything, it is important that this stage of development be handled carefully to ensure that problems do not occur.

If children are not allowed to use their counterwill to define themselves, they may develop masochistic-dependent capitulation and lack of self-identification—as discussed above—or an identification with the aggressor. Masochistic-dependent capitulation and lack of self-identification occur when children give up the idea of creating themselves and living a life that they enjoy and instead rely completely on others and live a life that does not give them pleasure from the things they desire as an individual. Identifying with the aggressor occurs when children wish to become dominant and controlling with others, the same way their parents are with them.

Additionally, children's adaptation to being denied use of their counterwill may involve both outcomes listed above, in two forms. With the first form, children may develop an outer-dependent capitulation with an inner-subordinate controlling impulse. These children appear externally as dependent on others, while internally they have powerful impulses of wanting control. With the second form, children may develop an outer-controlling position that thinly veils dependency. These children appear controlling and demanding to others, while internally they are going through an intense struggle with their urge to depend on others and allow others to make their decisions for them.

The difference between these four outcomes—masochistic-dependent capitulation and lack of self-identification, identification with the aggressor, outer-dependent capitulation with an inner-subordinate controlling impulse, and outer-controlling position that thinly veils dependency—in children who are not allowed to use their counterwill can be hard to thoroughly understand. Developmental and innate factors play a role in their ultimate fate.

Activity 3.16
Understanding Will

Complete the following activity to ensure that you have a good understanding of will. Match the terms on the left with their corresponding definition or example on the right.

1. Will
2. Desire to unite and be at one with others
3. Desire to create one's own self and life
4. Anxiety stemming from will
5. Guilt stemming from will
6. Creative individuation process
7. Counter-will
8. Masochistic-dependent capitulation / lack of self-identification
9. Identification with aggressor
10. Outer dependent capitulation with inner subordinate controlling impulse
11. Outer controlling position that veils dependency

a) Ahlam does not want to "fit in": she wants to do things that make her happy and make her own choices
b) Jody joined a book club because her mother said so, even though she does not like reading
c) Fear that previous attachments will be damaged when we separate from them
d) Impulse to act on personal desires, to affect our world, and create ourselves
e) Process of becoming separate and unique individuals
f) Tiffany believes that she should be in charge of making all decisions in her family, the same way her mother did
g) Lilly tells others what to do without listening to their opinion but wishes she could rely on others to make her decisions
h) Fears of loss and abandonment as we individuate
i) Initial way of defining self and creating an independent identity
j) Jay depends on his father to make all his decisions for him but also wishes he could make all his sister's decisions for her
k) Huda wants a connection with others and to feel as if she belongs

Negative Inner Will

Counterwill can lead to an individual developing a negative inner will. A negative inner will (LO, pp. 63-66) resists both surrendering to others and the individuation impulse. The negative will desires the opposite of the will's impulse to act on our personal desires and creates a negative, usually unconscious, impulse in the lower self to say "no" to life, accomplishment, and growth, surrender. Individuals with a strong "no" current believe that if their negative self-will is threatened then their separate existence is also threatened. Good feelings such as accomplishments and growth seem to be heralds of danger and a betrayal of the self.

Negative inner will may begin to form an organized way of cleverly defeating aspects of life in a mistaken effort to preserve the self. Furthermore, an individual may tend to destroy any sense of love, life, or growth that it experiences, with the belief that this is the way to protect oneself from harm. "If I don't love, I won't be hurt." Deep down, everyone has some element of a negative inner will that contributes to self-sabotage and negativism toward what is good in life. In other words, we all have a part of ourselves that does things we know will hurt us and avoids or destroys things in life that will benefit us. Those of us who have a lot of negative inner will lead very troubled lives. Conversely, those of us who only have a little negative inner will lead mostly happy and healthy lives of engagement, growth and fulfillment.

In most depth psychotherapies, this negative inner will is often unearthed, leading to a fundamental choice for the individual. The individual can listen to and give into the negative inner will or can attempt to counteract this impulse. By counteracting the impulse, the individual is choosing life, health, and happiness. It is an existential choice that is made from our free will—our ability to make choices and decisions based on our own preferences. We can choose to live a positive life-affirming life or a negative life-defying life.

Self-examination to discover this negative inner will has to proceed in the direction of sensing the self-defeating current that each of us has inside. Self-reflection when things don't go well in life should focus on what we are doing to say no to a solution to our problem, to our self-care and success instead of the quick impulse to blame others or life for our problems. Blaming others makes us the victim instead of revealing opportunities for change. Our only fault in a situation may be that we have chosen a friendship, or love, or work situation based on wishful thinking or trying to make life fit our expectations rather than seeing reality clearly. However, many times we find ourselves mysteriously repeating negative situations because we don't see what many people around us feel is right in front of our nose. Our negative will won't accept reality; it tries to make our illusions real, which just doesn't work. For example, believing someone is not mean to us when they are doesn't really make them not mean. It is better to see that the person is mean and make better decisions to confront the person or leave a bad relationship behind.

Making this choice regarding negative inner will can only be made when the negative inner will is fully unearthed. Furthermore, the choice can only be made once the negative inner will is fully discovered, explored, and understood. Otherwise we are only superimposing choice over the negative inner will or attempting growth by simply prohibiting symptoms. When this happens, the negative inner will is still just as present as it was before, causing negative impulses to continue to occur. Individuals must truly understand the effect their negative self-will has on them and their lives before they can make the choice to not give in to these impulses. When we do not have this understanding, we engage in a constant battle with ourselves of consciously wanting to say "yes" to adulthood and life while unconsciously saying "no." Unless the negative inner will is completely exposed to the individual, it will continue to sabotage any attempt the individual makes at adulthood and living a life-affirming life. This sabotage will discourage individuals from making any future efforts to say "yes."

Making the choice clear can be helped along by activating the negative inner will or the "no" to life in therapy. This can be done by playfully exaggerating your "no" to the positive in life. For example, it may take a long time for someone to unearth the feeling of being undeserving of a good relationship or a promotion. Being aware of "no, I don't believe I deserve to graduate or the love of this particular person" can be very liberating. It can then open up a desire to resolve our sense of feeling undeserving, or guilt or fear of a positive outcome. By allowing awareness of the negative inner will to build more and more, individuals are better able to see the negative impact it is having on them. They can then gain a sense of how saying "no" is holding them back from life and happiness. Thus, they can see more clearly the innate passion for life that they have denied and can fully embrace their desire for a life-affirming life.

An example of fear of punishment as a negative inner will is a hidden feeling that people may be envious if you write a book or a poem or a piece of art and may reject or abandon you. An example of not wanting to put in the work may be the actual time and sacrifice it takes to write a story. Sometimes people forsake goals in order to punish parents, even dead parents, who wanted them to accomplish a goal. Another negative subterfuge is not wanting to exceed a parent's standing because of guilt or a message that you are acting too full of yourself if you exceed your station in life. A friend who was born a cockney in London told me it was hard for a cockney to socially aspire because members of the community would think," What, are you too good for us? You want to do well and leave your community?"

Activity 3.17
Experiencing Your Negative Inner Will
This exercise is designed to help you activate your negative inner will. Spend a moment thinking of your goals, things you really want to accomplish or attain in life such as having a supportive relationship, fantastic job, great friends, or financial stability. Write each of your goals on a line below.

After recording your goals, explore your negative will related to each goal. Try to honestly connect with your "no," the part of you that sees a benefit in not achieving each goal, that doesn't want to put in the work to achieve the goal, that is mad about having to work hard for it, or that is afraid of not deserving the goal and being rejected or punished if it is actually accomplished. Read the following example before completing the activity for yourself.

Goal: I want to stop drinking and smoking.
Negative Will: I would miss out on good times if I did not drink as much and would lose out on the pleasure I get from smoking.

Goal: _____

_____

Negative Will:

_____

_____

Goal: _____

_____

Negative Will:

_____

_____

Goal: _____

_____

Negative Will:

_____

_____

***

When individuals struggle with their negative inner will and desire to change, they often question how to choose life instead of illness. When they say that they can't change, they are saying they want their illness to change but they themselves do not want to change; rather, they want the world to magically change around them. These individuals need to continue to bring out the "no" until they can clearly see the choice point between negative inner will and positive intent. Their will needs to be invested in their exploration and understanding of the "no" before they eventually will be able to make a more passionate choice for commitment to change.

Self-Will

Self-will (LO, pp. 52-53) leads us to create fulfillment in life, but often at the expense of others. It is the small will of the ego that is pushy, compulsive, forcing, and pitted against life and others. The self-will is the part of us that must win and get away with it; otherwise it is tragic. Our self-will is what drives our perfectionistic desire to achieve, accomplish, or obtain something in a ruthless or compulsive manner. The following example illustrates the actions of someone with a strong self-will. Nick wants to get a promotion at work, but he knows that there is someone else who is first in line to receive it. Nick decides to sabotage his colleague's work to ensure that he gets the promotion instead of his colleague. This is an extreme example of an individual's self-will driving their decisions and actions. In this example, Nick was willing to do whatever it took to ensure that he obtained the promotion, even at the expense of someone else. Self-will also pertains to everyday micro compulsions such as demanding attention and expecting life to supply you with support, provisions, and empathy while you are unwilling to give these to others.

Activity 3.18
Discovering Forcing Elements in Your Personality

Along with any forcing elements in the personality, self-will usually causes the opposite of what the individual wants. Look over the following illustration to see how acting out of self-will can give us the opposite of what we want. Then complete your own experiences of acting out of self-will.

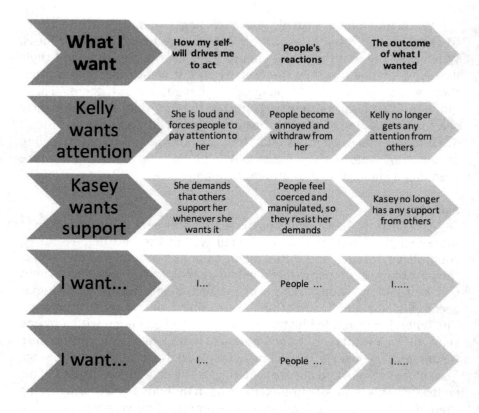

What I want	How my self-will drives me to act	People's reactions	The outcome of what I wanted
Kelly wants attention	She is loud and forces people to pay attention to her	People become annoyed and withdraw from her	Kelly no longer gets any attention from others
Kasey wants support	She demands that others support her whenever she wants it	People feel coerced and manipulated, so they resist her demands	Kasey no longer has any support from others
I want...	I...	People ...	I.....
I want...	I...	People ...	I.....

Self-will and the feeling that you lack fulfillment of your desires will cause tragedy and tension in the personality. The tension over time can cause bodily tension and pain, and the pain then creates a vicious cycle of demanding more to ease the pain. As the vicious cycle progresses through life, it gets worse and worse unless and until it is addressed and worked through. The self-will and the negative inner will together represent a potent element that makes up much of the powerful force of the low self in the personality.

Chapter 4
Elements of Treatment

Felt Sense

Emotions are often experienced viscerally—in other words, in a physical sense. Embarrassment may cause an individual's face to become warm and red. Fear may be experienced with a tightening of the muscles and a desire to run away. Every person may experience each emotion differently. For example, one may describe excitement as having butterflies in their stomach, while another may use this same depiction to describe nervousness. Tuning into physical experiences and having these experiences validated can help individuals develop a felt sense. Having a felt sense (LO, pp. 69) is knowing and being aware of one's subjectivity, affect, and needs. Developing a felt sense can help enhance self-awareness, self-direction, and intuition.

Activity 4.1
Exploring Your Felt Sense
Try describing the visceral/physical experience you have when you experience certain emotions. If you cannot describe the experience right away, take a minute to try to remember how you felt. Close your eyes, think back to a time when you experienced a strong emotion. Starting with your toes, work your way up to your head. Spend time on each body part, reflecting on how your body feels at this moment, while you re-experience a strong emotion from the past. Write the emotion that you are experiencing and then record the physical sensation that you feel on the line beside it.

Example: Anger: I feel my heart beating fast, my shoulders feel heavy, my fists are clenched, my forehead is scrunched.

_____ : _____

_____

_____ : _____

_____

_____ : _____

_____

***

Basic Rule

In the liberation of the core self, we strive to engage the most far-reaching aspects of the self; however, these aspects are not always conscious. In order to reach these aspects, a term called *free association* can be used to employ the basic rule of psychoanalysis (LO, pp. 80). The basic rule is that a client says anything and everything that comes to mind, without leaving anything out. By using free association, we can examine and explore elements that are in our unconscious. We can identify and explore aspects of our personality that have been hidden, which leads to the surrender of our ego to our healthy involuntary processes. This can be done as a form of self-analysis.

Activity 4.2
Practice Using Free-Association

Think of any issue, disturbance, or problem you are experiencing. Be still and then let whatever thoughts you have come to your mind. Some maybe be joyously ecstatic, some frightening and yucky. Whatever they are, let them come. After you do this for a while, you can rise and record them electronically or on paper.

When all this is written down, stop and feel into how your associations are related to your problem. Then try to connect how any of your faults—such as dependency, anger, envy, need for control or perfection—contribute to your problem. Your faults may have made a small problem larger or led you into the problem like a moth to a flame.

Problem_____

_____

_____

Associations_____

_____

_____

See how your faults and shadow feelings are causally connected to your problem or to the problem's exaggeration or continuance

_____

_____

_____

_____

_____

Determine what positive corrective action you can take going forward that will help you.

_____

_____

_____

_____

_____

***

Affect

Our affect (LO, pp. 70-72, 78, 119, 125) or feelings stem from our life force and are what vitalizes us. When we do not have feelings, we are simply conscious beings who are dead on the inside. After experiencing trauma of any type or magnitude, we create a state of traumatic living. In this state of traumatic living, our affect and life force become deadened as a way for us to handle the hurt and pain that comes with the trauma. Even if we are anxious and have flashbacks, our capacity for joy and zest is deadened. The healthier the childhood development we have, the less we feel the need to deaden ourselves, adopt neurotic defenses, and act out our negative feelings. Even those who have supportive, loving parents, and a healthy development are bound to experience some type of hurt or pain throughout their life. This pain causes distortions, twists our life force, and leads to numbness, which turns into psychological problems.

The affective numbing occurs when we deaden ourselves based on our personal histories and our abilities to cope with our history. For example, if a young girl is put up for adoption because her parents do not want her, she may feel a whole array of emotions such as hurt, confusion, or shame—along with the thought that there is something wrong with her. As she moves from foster home to foster home, constantly being rejected by her caregivers, she may eventually forbid herself from feeling hurt, confused, or ashamed. She may then numb her emotions and have a flat or nonexistent affect, because not feeling is less painful than the feelings she was experiencing.

When affect is explored, we can become more aware of our inner experiences. An individual can have more than one affect at a time; these affects can be separate from one another, or they can impact one another and become one. For example, recall the young girl from above. Her affect of hate toward her current foster parents may be connected to the shame of not feeling worthy of love from her biological parents. Her affect of shame may be the aftermath of hurt. In the end, the base affect from which all other affects stem is love. The young girl feels shame and hate because she experienced hurt and rejection when she desired love and acceptance. This is love outraged. By accepting all aspects of ourselves and all of our affects, even negative or painful ones such as hate and shame, we can return to our base affect, love.

Activity 4.3
Naming Your Emotions

Complete the diagram below. Start with the top arrow and write the name of the affect that you are experiencing. Think about this emotion and what it means, what it accomplishes for you, where it came from, and whether there is another emotion underlying this one. Record your thoughts in the box next to your emotion. Then move down to the next arrow, write the underlying emotion that you have just identified in the arrow. Continue this process, using another piece of paper if needed, as you work through the different affects that you have numbed as a result of your experiences. Continue this process until you reach your base emotion, love.

For example, a person who was chronically neglected as a child may have anger on the top line, shame on the second, hurt below the shame, then longing for love at the bottom or base.

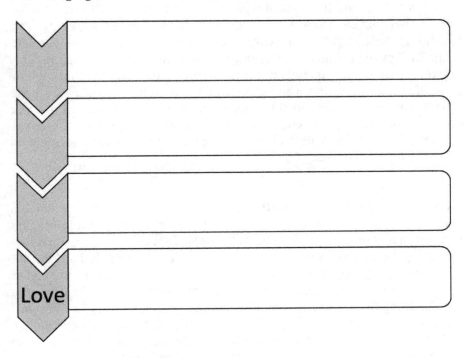

***

Pathogenic Beliefs

Throughout our lives, starting when we are children, we are constantly learning, and much of what we learn comes from our experiences. Our experiences influence us in many ways, one of which is how we interact with and view the world. Children develop a set of beliefs based on their childhood experiences. Pathogenic beliefs (LO, pp. 75-77) are similar to these beliefs based on experience; however, pathogenic beliefs are learned from a psychic injury. A psychic injury (LO, pp. 6, 75, 168) is a mental impairment or dysfunction that interferes with your ability to function. The suffering we endure from the experience in which our psychic injury occurred is so painful that we start to believe that all similar experiences will also result in suffering. It is then, based on this pathogenic belief, that we begin to see the double expression of needs and feelings.

For example, Sasha, a young girl abandoned by her father, may develop the pathogenic belief that all men whom she loves will abandon her. Because Sasha's desire for affection and love was met with abandonment and hurt, she developed a sense of distrust and hate for her father that can then become generalized to all males. Consequently, although Sasha still consciously longs for affection and love, she will unconsciously be afraid of feeling abandoned and hurt again. This leaves Sasha with an unconscious conflict based on her pathogenic belief that all men whom she loves will abandon her. These pathogenic beliefs are carried with us throughout our lives and are often at the root of our relational problems as we begin to generalize the experience. Recognizing these beliefs and challenging them is a core element in liberating the core self.

Activity 4.4
Pathogenic Beliefs Exploration
There are many psychic injuries that can occur at any point in life and result in any number of pathogenic beliefs. Choose one of the universal pathogenic beliefs listed below that fits with you or record a different pathogenic belief that you have discovered. In the box labeled "Pathogenic Belief," name and describe the pathogenic belief that you hold. Move back up to the top box labeled "Psychic Injury" and record the psychic injury that you believe is the root of this pathogenic belief. Now moving down to the bottom boxes labeled "Prior Influences" and "Current Influences," record how this pathogenic belief has influenced your life and how it is influencing your life right now.

Universal Pathogenic Beliefs:

- If I am not first, I am nothing.
- Others should always pay attention to me.
- It is important to win every time.
- I must be perfect to be loved and happy.
- I must worry about dangerous things to prevent them from happening.
- If people do not love me, they should be punished.
- People are either good or bad.
- I am small and weak and need others to take care of me.

Psychic Injury:

Pathogenic Belief:

Prior Influences:

Current Influences:

Once you have recognized these beliefs, take time to acknowledge their existence, challenge their truth, and explore the ways you can reconstruct them to help you grow individually and relationally.

***

The Use of Needs in the Liberation Process

Needs Versus Feelings

It is important to note the distinction between needs and feelings. Before distinguishing between needs and feelings, it is worth noting that in psychological terms feelings are referred to as affect. Therefore, the words affect, and feelings can be used interchangeable in this sense. More specifically, affect, referring to feelings and emotions, is a state that someone experiences either consciously or unconsciously. When experiencing a certain affect such as sadness, happiness, or anger, we are not motivated to take action or reach satisfaction. However, once we are pressed to take action, our affect then becomes a need, such as a need to cry, laugh, or lash out at someone. Affect can be viewed as a precursor of a need, which develops when an individual's feelings become intense. For example, someone may be fearful but not feel the need to seek safety; however, as this fear intensifies, they may develop the need to find safety.

Healthy Versus Unhealthy Needs

We experience healthy and unhealthy needs, both of which are motivational impulses. Healthy needs (LO, pp. 78, 90) help with emotional growth, self-care, affect regulation, and empathetic appreciation of others. Unhealthy needs (LO, pp. 77-84, 88, 118) are based on issues of power, appearances, and vanity and are harmful to the self and others. In contrast to healthy needs, which are necessary for emotional balance and well-being, unhealthy needs work against emotional balance and well-being. Overall, healthy needs work toward the love for self and others while unhealthy needs work against love for self and others.

Unhealthy Needs as Being Against Others

There is an infinite number of needs that we experience, both healthy and unhealthy. Imagine needs on a continuum from healthy needs to unhealthy needs. When healthy needs start to intermingle with egoism and hostility, they develop into unhealthy needs that become focused on defeating or going against others. All unhealthy needs hold the mentality of me-against-the-world. Being against others or against ourselves are both elements of the low self. An example is when someone's attempts to fulfill their healthy need for affection develops into submission as they try to please others. This submission then evolves into manipulation and seduction turning, a healthy need for affection into an unhealthy need for power.

Unhealthy Needs as Being Out of Time

Unhealthy needs can also evolve from healthy needs as a result of time. More specifically, when childhood needs are not fulfilled, they can carry over into adulthood and become unhealthy needs. For example, children have a need for love, and they desire a caregiver who will provide them with the care, time, and affection to fulfill this need. When children do not receive these behaviors from their caregivers, they continue into adulthood trying to fulfill this need. If it remains unfulfilled, their need for love will become distorted. This distorted love can evolve into an unhealthy need such as a need for punishment, anger, or isolation. It is not until the pain and suffering of the unmet need for love is addressed, explored, and mourned that the unhealthy need can dissolve.

Displaced Needs

Oftentimes when a need is not met, we will look for another need to take its place. When we are not able to fulfill a specific need, we displace our need for one thing onto another (LO, pp. 95). For example, imagine the child described above who has a need to be loved. This child may choose to repress their need for love as a way of trying to avoid the pain that comes with not feeling loved. However, needs do not go away when they are repressed; rather, they come back even stronger. This child may unconsciously begin searching for and demanding any type of attention to replace the need for love. Despite the amount of attention this child gets, it will never be enough because attention cannot fulfill the need for love. It is when this search for attention becomes compulsive that this need becomes unhealthy.

Substituted Needs

We can also try to cope with unmet needs by trying to substitute them for their opposite (LO, pp. 85). The child imagined above may substitute a need for withdrawal to compensate for the unmet need for love. This can be done in an attempt to protect ourselves with the idea that if we do not desire love we will not be hurt when we do not receive it. In addition to withdrawing, the child may also become hateful to others as a way of dealing with the pain. The unhealthy need to be hateful and mean to others would have replaced the healthy need for desiring love and affection from others.

Needs in Conflict

Have you ever had two things that you really wanted to do, but they were both happening at the same time, so you had to choose one or the other? Just like we sometimes have conflicts with our schedules, we can also have conflicts with our needs (LO, pp. 86, 89). Needs may conflict when fulfilling one need means not fulfilling the other. Just as the number of needs is limitless, there is also an infinite number of ways that needs can conflict. For example, Katie may have the need to be independent to prove to others that she can do things on her own, but also have a need to be in a relationship where she can depend on her partner. While in this scenario, Katie may be consciously aware of her two needs, there are times when we are not aware of our needs that are conflicting. For example, a career-oriented man may unconsciously have a need for love and affection but consciously believe that he should focus on making money in order to be happy. Just like the child discussed previously, his need for love and affection may have been repressed because it was not met during his childhood. Consequently, when his unconscious need for love is not fulfilled, he may put all of his energy and time into his work, further withdrawing and pushing people away.

Needs in Compromise Formation

When needs are in conflict, choosing one need or the other is not the only option; rather, needs in conflict may result in compromise formations (LO, pp. 87). Compromise formation occurs when two needs are in conflict and instead of completely fulfilling one while completely discounting the other, you choose to act in a way that leaves each need only partially fulfilled. For example, Katie may compromise her need for independence with her need for a dependent relationship by developing a relationship where she can depend on her partner emotionally but remain financially independent. There are as many ways to compromise needs as there are ways that needs can come in conflict. Coming up with a way to compromise your needs only takes the creativity to develop the compromise.

Needs in Harmony

Ideally, needs are in harmony (LO, pp. 88); however, the personality is influenced greatly by unconscious, conflicting, and compromised needs. Therefore, recognizing these needs can provide a complex and dynamic picture of our personality. This will allow our needs to be interpreted and confronted while we work toward transformation. Unhealthy needs can damage the personality, so it is important that our ego is able to contain and manage these unhealthy needs in a way that does the least amount of damage. Learning to manage and contain unhealthy needs is the first step in the transformation process, followed by compromise formations, which ultimately leads to harmonious needs. The ways that needs can be in harmony are as limitless as the ways that needs can be in conflict or be compromised. For example, a mother's need to work can be harmonized with her need to raise her children by working during the hours they are in school or working from home. Similarly, a need to eat healthy may harmonize with saving money in the form of starting a garden and growing your own vegetables. It is most favorable when needs are in harmony with one another because the more harmonious they are, the less conflict and more peace you experience.

Activity 4.5
Are Your Needs Being Fulfilled?
Think about your life as an out-picturing of your psychic state. Are your needs being fulfilled? Do you have the love you want? Do you have the friendships you want? Do you have a job that is meaningful for you and that you enjoy? Do you have enough recreation, exercise, and social time?

Really think about your needs and write down where your needs are fulfilled and where they are not. Below is a rudimentary list, which could be infinitely longer.

Healthy needs:	Aesthetic and self-actualizing needs:
Meaningful job	Culture and art
Good romantic relationship	Emotional growth
Positive friendships	Altruism
Good medical care	Humor or playfulness
Social time and activities	Creativity
Healthy sex life	Recreation
Enough sleep	Give to less fortunate
Enough healthy food	Community building
Enough exercise	Healthy self-assertion

Write down the areas of your life where you are fulfilled

_____

_____

_____

_____

_____

_____

Write down the areas of your life where your needs are unfulfilled

_____

_____

_____

_____

_____

_____

_____

Do unhealthy needs get in the way of or conflict with the fulfillment of any of your healthy needs? For example, an unhealthy need for entitlement may thwart your need for a good job and income. A need for control may hinder your need for a healthy romantic relationship. A need for perfectionism may hamper your need for fulfilling friendships.

Write down the unhealthy needs that conflict with fulfillment of the best in your life

_____

_____

_____

_____

_____

_____

_____

Challenge the unhealthy and conflicting needs that prevent fulfillment in your life. Take them to your meditation and affirm your desire to change them. For instance, if you have a need for perfectionism, to be critical, or to always be right, write about how they play into your troubles each day and try to let them go in favor of healthy needs. Let go of your need for self-pity, to be the victim, to be safely second, to disavow responsibility and affirm your need to achieve, to love, to be close, to be creative. Only don't just do this once but do it daily.

***

Prometheus Bound: Attachment to negative life situations
Most of us claim that we want to be happy, engage in positive situations, and experience pleasure in life. Nevertheless, while many of us consciously long for this pleasure, we go through life unconsciously avoiding it. This concept has been labeled *anhedonia* (LO, pp. 93), which refers to the avoidance of pleasure. The tendency to avoid pleasure is based on unconscious guilt that causes us to reject or say "no" to pleasure and fulfillment. If we automatically feel badly about ourselves and do not believe that we deserve good things in life, we will view ourselves as unloving and develop spite and envy toward others. Furthermore, when we have negative feelings toward others, whether consciously or unconsciously, we feel badly about ourselves, causing us to dislike ourselves and have low self-esteem. This cycle of feeling unloving, being hurtful to others, and then feeling negatively about ourselves is an automatic reflex that is inherent in all of us. This automatic reflex comes from our core self, which acts as a moral compass inside of us, registering any negativity. The core self-impulse becomes distorted by psychic and developmental injuries and turns on the self in judgment.

This suffering can be further understood through Aeschylus' myth of Prometheus (LO, pp. 92, 99-100). Prometheus was a titan who took pity on us mortals and gave us fire as a way to help us. This fire represents not only our ability to care for ourselves but also to create positive feelings and seek pleasure. Prometheus had stolen this fire from Zeus though, and Zeus punished Prometheus by chaining him to a rock and having an eagle peck out his liver every night. Prometheus' liver would grow back every day, making this an endless cycle of torture. This cycle of torture is similar to the cycle we described above regarding our negative actions and negative feelings. Prometheus' decision to steal fire in order to help mortals care for themselves was a crime, and that is how we view caring for ourselves as well. We believe that caring for ourselves is too dangerous and that if we do try to care for ourselves or reach for pleasure, we will be punished.

The Prometheus Chain
Just as Prometheus is chained to a rock, we, too, are chained by the influences that our early experiences have had on us (LO, pp. 102). We become chained by parental injunctions that keep us from self-care, pleasure seeking, and liberation. In order to break this chain and reach

liberation, there are seven links that must be understood and worked through. The seven links are (a) childhood hurt, (b) love outraged, (c) childhood omnipotence, (d) low self-esteem and unconscious guilt, (e) seeking punishment, (f) paranoid projection, and (g) compulsive dependency. This section of the book is broken into seven parts, with each section addressing a link in the chain. Within each section is a brief description of the link and an exploration of how we may currently be affected by this link.

Childhood Hurt

Children have a need to be loved, cared for, and supported by their parents, and when these needs are not fulfilled, they suffer some type of injury. Many parents struggle to provide their children with the love and affection they need. While the degrees of neglect and hurt vary, no parent is perfect, and therefore all children deal with some type of injury, abuse, or neglect. These negative experiences make up the first link in the chain, representing *childhood hurt* (LO, pp. 106-120).

We often try to forget or pretend like our childhood hurt did not happen because it is so painful. But one way to discover and explore our childhood hurt is by examining our current relationships. This is because childhood hurt does not simply go away; rather, it stays with us and pops up in our adult relationships or current problems. We unconsciously try to fix our childhood hurt by re-enacting or recreating the difficulties we had as children and our childhood hurt. There are many ways that this can be done, but a common way is by playing out the relationships we had with our parents in our romantic relationships. For example, we may choose a romantic partner who has the similar positive aspects of our parents but who also has the similar negative aspects that caused our childhood hurt. When we do this, we set ourselves up to continue experiencing as adults the hurt that we received during childhood.

Love Outraged

When children do not receive the love and affection they desire, they respond with anger. This anger response is the second link in the chain, known as *love outraged* (LO, pp. 6, 33-34, 45-46, 50, 56, 102, 107, 113, 126, 154, 162, 164, 167, 172). When their desire to be loved is not fulfilled, children respond instinctively by becoming angry or outraged, hoping that this will change their situation. However, instead of providing their child with the love and affection that is the root of the anger, parents often shame their child for this behavior. This furthers the parent's belief that their child is bad and needs to be punished.

Children do not always consciously register the hurt they experience because they do not have the verbal memory needed to do so. Verbal memory allows us to use words to represent or symbolize our experiences and feelings. Our verbal memory allows us to understand our experiences and feelings more fully. Children may instead rely on their limbic or emotional memory, which is a part of the brain that records and remembers experiences emotionally. Imagine a boy named Deshawn whose dad left him and his family when he was young. Although Deshawn was not able to put words to his experience at the time, he unconsciously remembered that it hurt him. Children unconsciously register how a certain event or situation made them feel but are unable to understand it in the same we are able to as adults.

As adults we may not consciously remember our childhood hurt, but we unconsciously carry this hurt and the anger it causes us into adulthood. Later in life, Deshawn may become extremely anxious anytime someone leaves for a period of time or is not emotionally available to him, experiencing a fight-or-flight response. Deshawn's fight response is that he is angry that someone is leaving him, while his flight response is fear. Deshawn becomes angry because he unconsciously remembers the hurt that he experienced when his father left him as a child. But since he does not remember the actual event behind this hurt, he is not able to understand the underlying reason for his fear. This anger and confusion affects our personality as we interpret, respond, and experience similar events in a certain way. This influences our view of ourselves, along with how we view and interact with others and the world in general.

Childhood Omnipotence

The anger and outrage that children have toward their parents, as noted earlier, results in *childhood omnipotence* (LO, pp. 103, 105, 108), the third link in the chain. This idea of childhood omnipotence does not mean that the child is omnipotent or that the child believes he or she is omnipotent; rather, the child feels entitled to be omnipotent. Furthermore, when parents are not fully engaged, children do not experience the attention, affection, and support they desire, and they can become fixated on receiving this positivity and availability. Because their needs were not fulfilled in childhood, children experience childhood omnipotence—the belief that they are entitled to have their unlimited demands for love and attention met.

Although this belief stems from the lack of parental involvement in the child's life, this belief in entitlement extends well beyond their parents, with children believing that the world and everyone in it should put them first. Children go through life believing that their needs and desires should always be met. When they are not met, children experience the world as bad and believe that others need to be punished so that they can fulfill their own needs. As adults, the demands of our childhood omnipotence are impossible to fulfill, causing us to experience a cycling of anger throughout life. We are angry when we do not receive enough attention. We are angry when others need us too much. We are even angry when our friends expect mutual care and support from us. This omnipotence goes beyond our relationships, as we become angry whenever anything does not go our way, such as the weather being too hot or too cold. This omnipotence is never fully conscious because we know deep down that our demands are unreasonable and childish. We do not want others to see our sense of entitlement because we are embarrassed by it. We don't even want to admit it to ourselves because we are ashamed of our omnipotence.

Low Self-esteem and Unconscious Guilt

The shame and embarrassment we experience because of our childhood omnipotence cause us to have *low self-esteem* and *unconscious guilt* (LO, pp. 6, 92, 95, 103, 105, 109, 111, 151), the two aspects that make up the fourth link in the chain. The guilt that we experience comes from our core self and our internal moral compass that was previously discussed. Whether consciously or unconsciously, we feel guilty when we have negative thoughts toward others or when we treat others negatively. Additionally, our unconscious negativity can cause us to feel guilty about numerous things, even things that we should not feel guilty about. We can trace this unconscious guilt back to the beginning links in the chain: the anger we felt toward our parents for the childhood hurt we experienced. As a way of coping with the real guilt we feel for being angry with our loved ones, we begin to develop a false sense of guilt for things that are out of our control.

Our unconscious belief that we are guilty can cause us to believe that we are bad. We believe that we do not deserve happiness and that we deserve to be punished. This causes a conflict in our personality. We want to experience happiness and pleasure but fear that we do not deserve this sense of fulfillment in our lives. To cope with this conflict, we start to compromise by acting in ways that prevent us from being entirely happy or successful. For example, we may unconsciously procrastinate so that even if we succeed at what we are doing we can still be shamed for our tardiness. When we are doing well or winning at something, we may unconsciously sabotage ourselves by becoming anxious and slowing down our efforts so that we fail or at least come in second. The guilt that we carry around and our inability to allow ourselves to experience success or pleasure impact our self-esteem or the way we feel about ourselves. Even if we try to view ourselves positively or accomplish positive things, the unconscious feeling that we are guilty, bad, and underserving of happiness is so strong that we cannot possibly have high self-esteem.

Seeking Punishment

Oftentimes this feeling of guilt and low self-esteem comes with the belief that we need to be punished. There is a sense of shame and helplessness that makes us feel that life is going to punish us in some way, no matter what. In order to cope with this belief, we respond by taking this punishment into our own hands. The act of *seeking punishment* (LO, pp. 103-104, 110-111) is the fifth link in the chain. We decide that since we will be punished regardless, we might as well punish ourselves before others have the chance. This is an attempt to prove to ourselves and others that we have at least some control over our lives and provide us with some degree of dignity.

We discredit ourselves, laugh at ourselves, and criticize ourselves before others have the chance to. For example, have you ever completed a project or assignment that you thought was really good, but when showing it to others you made sure to say "it's not very good" or point out parts that you thought were bad? Have you ever made a suggestion then followed it up with "that's a dumb idea" before giving anyone the chance to offer you feedback? These are all ways in which we seek to punish ourselves because we believe that if we don't others will.

Paranoid Projection

The sixth link in the chain consists of *paranoid projection* (LO, pp. 112), which is similar to seeking punishment. When we are not able to punish ourselves with our own aggression, we use paranoid projection as a defense. Paranoid projection is the idea that when we are not able to accept the negative aspects of ourselves, such as envy or anger, we project these aspects onto others. The negativity that we have not been able to work through becomes an unconscious belief that others are aiming these negative thoughts at us.

It is difficult to recognize and accept our own faults, and when we are not able to do this we cope by projecting these faults onto or attributing them to others. Instead of admitting that we are envious of someone, we decide that they must be envious of us. When we are judgmental, we believe that they are actually the ones judging us. We project our own jealousy onto others, telling ourselves that they are jealous of us. When we go through life projecting these negative feelings onto others, we set ourselves up to be re-injured just as we were as children. In other words, we believe that any type of achievement or self-care we experience will be met with negative feelings such as judgment, envy, contempt, or anger.

Compulsive Dependency

All of the links in the chain that we have explored so far lead up to the seventh link, *compulsive dependency* (LO, pp. 104, 123). The unconscious guilt and low self-esteem that we hold because of our anger, followed by trying to punish ourselves or projecting onto others the belief that others only hold negative feelings toward us merely furthers our need for the love and approval that we so greatly desired during childhood. We become even more dependent on others to make us feel loved, valued, and important.

Just as the needs of our childhood omnipotence were unreasonable, being so dependent on others makes it impossible for them to fulfill our needs. This compulsivity will then only further our anger toward others, causing us to feel rejected, view ourselves negatively, and make us more vulnerable to the hurt and anger that cause us unconscious guilt. This vicious cycle continues, enhancing our belief that we are not good or lovable and consequently causing us to avoid happiness, pleasure, or fulfillment by seeking out negative experiences.

Breaking the Chain

There are various techniques that can be used to break the different links of the Promethean chain. However, before working through these techniques, it is important to understand *negative capability* (LO, pp. 2, 5, 104) and *self-reflection* (LO, pp. 2, 7, 104-105, 133, 144). Negative capability and self-reflection are two elements that are central to being able to break the chain that binds us. Negative capability is the ability to leave behind the narrow perspectives we have of ourselves and explore new understandings of events or context. In other words, negative capability allows us to no longer view ourselves in only a positive way. Rather, we are able to view ourselves in a new sense, one that recognizes and accepts both positive and negative aspects of ourselves. Having this sense of negative capability allows us to be comfortable with any doubt or uncertainty we may have while self-reflecting. Self-reflection is when we suspend the judgments we hold about ourselves and how we believe we should be in order to see ourselves for who we really are.

Overall, negative-capability and self-reflection allow us to develop a more comprehensive idea of who we are by remaining open to all possibilities and not being afraid of what it is we may find while exploring ourselves and our experiences. Several activities are listed below based on an array of different techniques. Some activities are designed for specific links in the chain, while other activities are more general. However, you can apply any of these activities to whichever link in the chain that you feel would be helpful. As you explore and work through the different activities and links of the Promethean chain, try to use negative capability and self-reflection to their fullest extent.

Childhood Hurts

An important step in working through the Promethean chain is to discover our childhood hurt. We can discover the childhood hurt that we have been repressing by examining problems in our current relationships and exploring the emotional relationship that we have with our parents.

Activity 4.6
Discovering Childhood Hurts

Complete the following three parts of this activity, remembering to apply the concepts of negative capability and self-reflection.

Part 1: Current Relationships
In the space below, record any problems that you are aware of in your current relationships. While these problems are often seen in romantic relationships, they can also be present in many other types of relationships. Read the examples below showing the different types of relationships and the different kinds of problems and then fill in your own.

Example: Romantic Relationship—I do a lot for my partner because I really care about him, but he says that I need to give him more space and is constantly telling me that if I don't stop acting like his mother, he is going to leave me.

Example: Work Relationship—I just quit my job because of how my boss treated me. I always work extra hours, take on extra tasks, and make sure they are done perfectly and on time; but I am never acknowledged for it. So, when a promotion for the company opened up, I decided to just quit because I knew that I wouldn't get it since my boss doesn't appreciate all that I do. This same thing has happened to me twice before because I would rather quit than have someone else who doesn't do as much for the company get chosen over me. Now try this approach with one of your own relationship problems.

1._____:_____

_____

_____

2._____:_____

_____

_____

3._____:_____

_____

_____

Activity 4.6

Part 2: Child–Parent Relationship
Try to reflect back on what your relationship with your parents was like. It is easy to say that you had loving parents and a good childhood, but no parent or childhood is perfect. Read the questions below, take time to truly reflect on them, and record any significant findings you may have in the space provided. All of these questions may not apply to you, and there may be parts of your relationship with your parents that are not covered in the questions provided. Use these questions as a guide or a starting point, but feel free to record anything that comes to mind. A couple of examples have been provided to illustrate how one might interpret and respond to these questions.

A. Who took care of who in the relationship? Did you go to your
    parents when you needed help? Did your parents depend on you a
    lot?

    Example: I remember my mom as always being either very sad or
    extremely happy. When I was a kid, I hated seeing her sad, so I
    would spend all of my time with her trying to cheer her up. Looking
    back now, I hate to admit it, but I think I actually liked when she was
    sad because this is when we spent the most time together. It seemed
    like she needed me when she was sad. But when she was happy, she
    was always going out with her friends and never around, so I never
    got to see her. So, I guess she never really took care of me because
    either she was too sad and needed me to take care of her or she was
    off doing her own thing.

B. Were your parents proud of you? Did they hang your drawings on
    the fridge, congratulate you when you got a good test grade, brag
    about you to their friends?

    Example: My parents were proud of me but not the same way that
    they were proud of my brother. I always worked super hard in
    school to get good grades, but my brother always seemed to be
    better and more important. They were always talking to their
    friends about how good my brother was at football and always
    thought that his games were more important than my schoolwork.
    My parents threw a huge party for my brother when he got an offer
    to play football in college without a scholarship, but only took me
    out to dinner when I got a full ride to college through an academic
    scholarship.

C. How did your parents respond when you cried? Were you told not
    to cry? Did they talk to you about your feelings? Were you sent to
    your room?

D. Did your parents let you make decisions for yourself or were you
    always forced to do what your parents wanted you to?

E. Were you allowed to complain or become angry without being
    criticized, shamed, or punished?

F.   Were your parents able to enjoy you? Did they spend time with you? Were they happy when they were around you? Did they always seem mad when you were together?

G.   Did your parents give you everything that you wanted? Were you ever told no? How did you react if you were told no?

My findings: _____

_____

_____

_____

_____

***

Activity 4.6

Part 3: Making Connections

Read what you recorded in the first two parts of this activity. Do the current problems in your relationships have anything in common with the relationship you had with your parents? Try to think how you felt when you were in those relationships or how you feel about them now. Does your current partner act like and treat you like your parents did? Do you treat your partner as you treated your parents? Based on the examples provided previously in the activity, read the example below showing how you may be able to make a connection between the hurt you experienced as a child and the problems that you are currently having. Then record any connections that you make from your own experiences.

Example: I always thought that if I took care of my mom, she would want to be around me even when she didn't need me. But the same thing happened every time she got better; she just abandoned me. I treat my partner the same way I treated my mom by trying to do every little thing he needs because I think that if he realizes he needs me he won't leave. Every time we fight, I get the same scared feeling that I would get when I would notice my mom starting to get better. But I can't help but to be over-caring for him, even though I know it means he is not going to leave me like my mom always did.

Example: I try to be successful at work to please my bosses the same way I was successful in school in an attempt to please my parents. But just like my scholarship went unnoticed and wasn't appreciated by my parents, nothing I do at work ever gets noticed either. I always felt like I had to prove myself to my parents, and now I am still having to try and prove myself to my bosses. The difference, though, is that I am not going to let my bosses make me feel the way my parents always did, I'm not going to give them that chance.

My connections: _____

_____

_____

_____

_____

***

Playing with Aggression
In order to work through our love outrage and anger, we first have to admit that we have aggressive impulses and take responsibility for them as a problem. Anger is generally viewed as a negative emotion, making it something that people often do not want to admit to or talk about. Humor, on the other hand, is generally viewed positively, and conversations containing humor are usually much easier to have. We use humor as a way to create a safer, more comfortable space to explore our anger

Activity 4.7
Getting in Touch with Your Emotions

Use this brief activity as a way to become more comfortable with your emotions. Try to get in touch with your anger. Can you remember the last time you were angry or the time that you were most angry? Is there someone who makes you so angry you can barely stand them? Are there certain situations that always make you angry? On the next page, record several of the different experiences you can remember in which you were angry, had aggressive thoughts, or were aggressive.

_____

_____

_____

_____

_____

_____

Now make a statement expressing your outrage for each situation, but make them absurd and extreme to the point that they sound ridiculous to you.

Example: I won't take care of my mother, I'll put her in a home or abandon her. I'll just leave her to her misery and laugh at her for it. Ha, ha, ha. You are sick again. Well, it's because you deserve it.

_____

_____

_____

_____

_____

_____

This activity was intended to get you more comfortable with your emotions so that you can explore them more freely going forward. As we work through more activities, we will be referring to the experiences you have recorded here. It is important to be able explore your emotions in a way that goes beyond just knowing them; you should be able to truly own and experience them.

***

Recognizing and Accepting our Childhood Omnipotence
Similar to our angry impulses, recognizing and accepting our childhood omnipotence is a major turning point in our emotional and spiritual growth.

Activity 4.8
Effect of Childhood Omnipotence on Adulthood
Part 1: Discovering Childhood Omnipotence
Answer the following "yes" or "no" questions, being as honest with yourself as you can.

Do I know how to get my way? _____

When something does not go my way, do I rely on others to change things? _____

Do I feel like others owe me? _____

Do I usually get my way? _____

Is it difficult for me to compromise with others? _____

Do I feel entitled to a lot of things? _____

Am I spoiled by others? _____

Have I ever been called manipulative? _____

Is my happiness more important than that of others? _____

***

Part 2: Exploring Childhood Omnipotence Connection with your Problems
If you answered yes to the majority of the questions above, your childhood omnipotence may be influencing your life. Remember that childhood omnipotence means that you believe you are entitled to be omnipotent. Refer to the experiences you recorded in the previous activity. Do you think that your childhood omnipotence played a role in any of these experiences? If yes, explore the experience more fully by reflecting on the questions below. If no, try to think of an experience in which your childhood omnipotence did play a role and reflect on that experience using the questions below.

What events led to me becoming angry and act out?

_____

_____

Was it others' actions or my own actions that were more of the problem?

_____

_____

Was it because I did not get my way? Elaborate.

_____

_____

Why did I feel like I should have gotten my way in this situation? Did I have a rational reason?

_____

_____

Did I do anything to try to change the outcome of the situation, or did I believe it was someone else's responsibility?

_____

_____

How did I respond when I realized things were not going my way? Do I always act this way when something does not go my way?

_____

_____

Do I feel better after acting this way or do I feel worse? Is there another way I could have responded?

_____

_____

***

Part 3: Developing Causal Connections Between Childhood Omnipotence and Your Problems
Once you have reflected on the questions in Part 2, record a statement below regarding how your childhood omnipotence has caused or contributed to some of the problems you have had in your life.

Example: It contributed to the breakup of early positive relationships because I would become far too angry when girlfriends wouldn't take care of my needs well enough.

_____

_____

_____

_____

_____

_____

By recognizing and accepting our childhood omnipotence we can work to improve the unrealistic demands we set for others that often leave us angry and hurt. Going forward, continue recognizing and accepting the childhood omnipotence inside of you, but also make sure to remember that your recognition and acceptance can help you overcome this omnipotence.

Chapter 5
Transforming Duality

Transforming duality (LO, pp. 11, 14-15, 43, 126, 129, 161, 164, 175) is a process that focuses on our fears and anxieties with the goal of transforming them. The problems that we experience in life are often what we are afraid of and run away from due to fear. Transforming duality encourages people to face their fears and anxieties instead of running away from them. Moreover, it helps us experientially know that a place of non-fear of troubles and pains can be at least touched in this life. If every "problem" is thought of as a stepping stone to transformation, then when problems occur they can be felt and not just seen as an opportunity.

Activity 5.1
Using Problems as Opportunities

Complete this activity to understand your fears more fully, accept them, and use them as a stepping stone toward liberation. We can confront our fears by using each problem or difficulty we face as an opportunity to self-examine what it is we need to change in ourselves so that the problem does not return or we are able to cope with the problem if it does return. Write a current problem and what faults you need to face and change in yourself.

Example: My partner and I have been arguing because he wants to move in together, but I do not want to.

_____

_____

_____

_____

_____

_____

Activity 5.2
Connecting Underlying Fears to Current Problems

Try to think of your deepest fears. Are you afraid of failure? How about success? Are you afraid to be abandoned, that no one will love you, or that you do not know how to love? Do you fear you will let others down or that others will let you down? Do any of your fears have to do with your current life difficulty? Record your fear(s) below and how this fear is impacting your current problem.

Example: I am afraid to get too attached to anyone because if I do and someone leaves or dies, I would be devastated. This is impacting my life because I won't move in with my partner since I do not want to get more attached.

_____

_____

_____

_____

_____

Activity 5.3
How We Run from Our Fears

When we do not confront our fears, no matter how big or small, they impact our lives. When we run away from our fears, it causes a strain on our personality and we develop a desire to avoid life, both the positive and negative aspects. Record the different parts of life you have avoided by running from your fear(s).

Example: Negative aspects avoided: I have not had my heart broken or been extremely sad about a breakup.

Example: Positive aspects avoided: I have not been able to fully let my partner in; I have not been able to take the next step of living with my partner.
Part of life: _____

_____

Part of life: _____

_____

Activity 5.4
Further Understanding of Your Fears

Now that you are aware of the fear related to your current difficulty and how it influences you, how can you work to overcome this fear? Instead of viewing your situation as a problem, try to view it as a teaching or gift. Reflect on the questions below to understand how this life lesson can help with your self-transformation.

What led to your fear?

Have you experienced this problem before? What was the outcome?

_____

_____

Do you have pre-existing beliefs about this situation?

_____

_____

What do you need to grieve to give up your struggle?

_____

_____

What promethean link is binding you to your fear? Is it your childhood omnipotence of needing to get your way?

_____

_____

Is it your self-punishment because you think you deserve this struggle?

_____

_____

Is it a childhood hurt that has left you with this fear? Can you describe your hurt?

_____

_____

Do you have healthy needs that were buried that may be seen now? What are these needs?

_____

_____

What personal fault should you work on that is revealed by this problem, hurt, or revealed needs?

_____

_____

Activity 5.5
Developing Strategies to Overcome your Fears

Once you have explored and reflected on these questions, come up with a strategy that allows you to overcome your difficulty by choosing to confront your fear instead of running from it.

Strategy: _____

_____

_____

_____

_____

_____

Accepting that good can come from bad and that bad can come from good will allow you to live life more fully and positively instead of avoiding all experiences out of fear that they may lead to something negative.

Chapter 6
Conclusion

Understanding how important emotional growth is to our mental health and emotional well-being, Jamie and I were inspired to offer a second book in the Love Outraged series and worked hard to make the psychological material more user friendly and experience near. We have provided many psychological exercises, meditations, and affirmations that will help clarify material and provide you with a direct means to use the concepts to transform yourself. Some counselors may also choose to use the exercises to help them with their clients as well.

In the end, Jamie and I hope this workbook will be of some immediate additional aid and instruction to you on your path to emotional health, liberation, and freedom from fear. These concepts are not actually popular psychology; rather, they are concepts that require the person using this book to already have some self-awareness of their shadow, their higher self, and life's spiritual dimension—a spiritual dimension that is hidden behind our daily mass of illusions of conflict and strife.

The path to our core self and peace often requires the transformation of negativity and shadow elements that shroud the best and most splendorous within us and life. This is the steep and narrow way. But if the shadow work is skipped, peace and health will only be short lived or marginal at best. This is why we offer tools to discover, understand, and transform your shadow and lower self so your liberation will be real and enduring.

Our world of duality, conflict, and pain is created by each of our lower selves, which flow together collectively to create all that we experience around us. As we grow and work through our faults, hostilities, and projections, what we will see is that we will experience the world around us as ever more benevolent. To the extent that we reduce our hostility, we will feel that others will embrace and include us. However, this cannot be done in the form of lip service. We can act benevolently, but if we harbor hostility, it will sneak out and affect others, and we will experience our world at war.

This workbook and the original *Love Outraged* text are intended to reach and resolve troubled areas of our psyches at the emotional level. This is a deeper causal level of our personality and the world around us. Deep effective change has to touch and heal this unconscious level of our being. It is easy to say "I love you" and not mean it. It is easy to preach kindness but surreptitiously do the opposite. We all live in Plato's allegorical cave, where we see reflections or shadows rather than reality. What is inner becomes our outer experience. To the extent we live from love, our world will be loving. We have tried to circle around this truth, that we experience and create the world around us based on the total emanations of our personalities. Believe it or not, it is the truth, and we hope this book provides a tiny spark and bit of guidance for your journey.

Thanks for reading, and may you be inspired on your Path.

~ Franklin and Jamie

Glossary

Abyss of Illusion: A psychological experience within us in which we feel we are falling to our death if we don't get our way, people don't esteem or recognize us enough, and life and others can't be forced to do our bidding.

Acceptance: Fifth and final stage of the process to the ego acceptance state that results from accepting reality as it is until we can change it.

Acknowledgment: Second stage of the process to the ego acceptance state in which anger is acknowledged and begins to be understood.

Affect: A state someone experiences consciously or unconsciously; also known as feelings and emotions that stem from one's life force.

Affective Numbing: A psychological defense that involves deadening ourselves, which limits our feelings so that we can handle our hurt from the past.

Affirming the Existence of the Core Self: The therapeutic process of recognizing that each person has a core self whose loving qualities can make tolerable the negative transference and affective states that seem otherwise unbearable.

Allow the Experience: Third stage of the process to the ego acceptance state, which involves allowing ourselves to experience the pain that stems from our wishes and reality in order to discover that the pain is bearable.

Angry Dependency: Accrues from a neglectful or rejecting parental environment in which a person grows up needing to receive gratification of needs for caring, esteem, and narcissistic valuing way beyond healthy proportions, thus crippling their own needs for independence, autonomy and self-agency.

Anhedonia: Either an avoidance of or inability to experience pleasure.

Anxiety and Anger: First stage of the process to the ego acceptance state, which involves reacting negatively to others not acting how we want them too.

Arrogance and Vanity: Exaggerated and excessive sense of one's own importance, achievements, and abilities that is an attempt to rise above others as a way to resolve feelings of inferiority.

Augment Tolerance: Fourth stage of the process to the ego acceptance state when we begin to increase our ability to handle the pain we experience.

Basic Rule of Psychoanalysis: Liberation of the core employs the basic rule of psychoanalysis. The rule states that the client as much as possible says everything that comes to mind and tries not to edit anything out.

Character Faults: Distortions of the core self that reside within the lower self and are harmful to ideal personality development.

Childhood Hurts: Psychological harm stemming from early childhood trauma, neglect, maltreatment that often affects how people make choices, use defense mechanisms and form relationships in adulthood.

Childhood Omnipotence: A component of the Prometheus Chain, where one believes they are entitled to have all of their demands and needs met.

Compromise Formation: A Freudian concept where the instincts of aggression and sexuality may come into conflict, resulting in a state of partial gratification of each instinct or wish and partial non-gratification or unfulfillment.

Compulsive Dependency: A component of the Prometheus Chain, where one becomes exceedingly dependent on others to like them, reflect their values, be interested in them, and esteem and love them in order to lessen self-doubt.

Conscious Emotional Continence: Conscious emotional acceptance of all aspects of ourselves, including that which beforehand was considered unacceptable and unlovable, as the root of happiness.

Containment: A therapeutic outcome in which one gains an increased ability to tolerate their feelings, and in doing so gains self-esteem and confidence.

Contempt: Forms as a method of elevating ourselves when we feel bad about ourselves; a feeling that others are worthless, beneath us or deserving of scorn.

Core Self: The expansive foundational self in all human beings that rests in unitive experience of love and primary connectedness with others.

Cosmic Egg: Diagrammatic representation of the four elements of the self.

Counterwill: The natural human resistance to being controlled; the common "no" to a parent that a two-year-old evidences.

Death Anxiety: A feeling of dread, apprehension, or fearfulness when one thinks of the process of dying or ceasing to exist. Persistent fear of one's own death.

Defense Mechanism/Defense: Defense mechanisms are more than the classic repression and denial. They can be any negative or illusory state or feelings that keep us from deeper hurt, longing, and love.

Deficiency Needs: Also known as "d needs"; the most fundamental and basic four layers of Maslow's pyramid containing esteem, friendship and love, security, and physical needs. These needs must be met in order to allow someone to self-actualize.

Depth Psychology: A conceptualization and treatment of the personality based on dynamic and often unconscious motivational elements such as affect, impulses, needs drive, and wishes.

Denial: A primary defense mechanism distinguished by a refusal to acknowledge painful realities, thoughts, feelings, or past experiences. Wanting to pretend the painful experiences never happened.

Displaced Needs: When a real need is never gratified, a person can transfer the unmet need into a need to accomplish or obtain a substitute. Often a need for love becomes a displaced need for approval or achievement. Displaced needs never fix the original repressed hurt/need left unmet.

Duality: The state of being in two parts; the way we ultimately see the world and our existential world immersion that is largely unconscious—for example, good versus evil, right versus wrong, light versus dark.

Dying into Process: A surrender to the loss of a part of one's identity through sitting with psychically painful feelings that were previously avoided

Ego "I": The conscious and knowable part of the self that is in touch with reality and must manage impulses from both the id and the superego.

Ego Logic: Rational judgment, with intuitive or tacit knowledge less evident.

Ego Omnipotence: An inner psychological belief that we should be in charge of all that is around us; this leads us to try to force everything to fit our will, our wants, and our needs, including the desire to force others to love us, admire us, or put us first. Also known as the need for rulership.

Egocentricity: Holding the idea that one's self (ego) is the center, object, and norm of all experience.

Emanations of the Self: The diffusion of the self, meaning that the further away from the source, the more distortion of the core self there is (less divine, more negative versions of the self).

Emotional Dwelling: An empathic response in which the listener actively participates in the pain and suffering of the speaker.

Entitlement: Being fixated or stuck in a childish position of expecting and demanding the world and others become the good parent one didn't have; an eternal longing and demand that life be made comfortable and easy by others and an anger that arises when this is not met.

Envy: A feeling of discontent or resentment toward another person due to a desire for the possessions, relationships, or qualities of another. Envy contains hate in the form of wanting to spoil something about the person who is envied.

False Self: A personality structure that correlates with the idealized self and is developed to conform to the expectations of what others want and expect in the environment. Reads and conforms to the environmental/societal norms to be the most acceptable or perceived as behaving or being in the most glorified way.

Fear of Death: A phenomena experienced by everyone on the planet, a fear of one's own death or the process of his or her own dying. Associated with death anxiety: the persistent fear or dread of one's own death.

Felt Sense: The inner knowledge or awareness that has not been consciously thought or verbalized. A bodily experience of "knowing something."

Free Association: Technique used to explore and examine aspects of the unconscious. It can be used as a form of self-analysis.

Healthy Need: A motivational impulse in the service of emotional growth, self-care, affect regulation, and empathic appreciation of the other without which emotional balance and health is impaired. Healthy needs are in the service of love for self and others.

Higher Self: Taoist, Sufi and many modern spiritual/mystical theorists equivalent to the core self.

Hubris: Overbearing pride or presumption; arrogance.

Id "It": A person's internal drives and feelings; contains the instincts that include sex, aggression, self-preservation, and the death instinct. The part of the self that is unconscious and outside of awareness.

Id Resistance: A pull in the unconscious to stay attached to our problems. Can be a direct or indirect opposition to change.

Idealized Self: An unrealistically perfectionistic and self-aggrandizing defensive self, although possibly unconscious in nature, that is an attempt to deny vulnerability, shame, anxiety, and other dysphoric feelings. Correlates with the concept of false self.

Intentional and Organized Consciousness: An organized group of impulses that intentionally seek to defeat emotional growth, love, self-care, and the personality.

Liberate: To set free from oppression or suppression.

Libido: The psychic and emotional energy associated with the instinctual biological drives, emanating from the id. Primarily defined as sexual urges and desires.

Life Anxiety: The anxiety of losing oneself in being.

Life Force: The central energy and vitality that moves through all living things. In the unitive state, love is the life force that drives humans.

Life Stream: The enlivening forced behind all life that is pleasure and positive consciousness and at the deepest level is unified with all life.

Loss of Self: Either loss of the self in actuality or loss of the paranoid projection of the ego.

Love Outraged: The idea that all malicious anger and its derivatives such as revenge, hate, and negative aggression are expressions of the need for love being hurt and outraged in earlier development.

Low Self/The Shadow: The aspect of our personality that becomes distorted and misdirected so that love in various ways becomes permuted into hate, avarice, cruelty, or envy. Stemming from love outraged.

Low Self-esteem and Unconscious Guilt: A component of the Prometheus Chain, where people begin to view themselves negatively and hold the belief that they do not deserve anything good.

Lower Soul: Plotinus's conception of the part of the soul that is separated and has fallen into vices, character faults, and destructive patterns.

Marriage of Pleasure and Pain: Enjoyment in one's own pain of self-destructiveness, making self-pity, negative feelings, and self-defeating behavior difficult habits to give up.

Meaninglessness: A sense that the decisions and occurrences of life are devoid of any real significance; purposelessness in life.

Mourning Liberation Process: A process of freeing positive affect that is contained within negative affect or transforming negative affect to positive affect.

Moderated Expression: Coping technique employed by the strong ego that recognizes and replaces negative impulses with more assertive responses.

Needs in Conflict: When fulfilling one need prevents the fulfilling of another need, of which a person may or may not be consciously aware.

Negative Capability: The ability to remain with doubt and uncertainty when self-reflecting and not rush to easy ready-made answers. The capacities of human beings to reject the totalizing constraints of a closed context and explore new understanding of an event or context.

Negative Inner Will: Force in the personality that resists surrendering to others and individuation by saying "no" to all aspects of life.

Paranoid Projection: A component of the Prometheus Chain in which we are unable to accept the negative view we hold of ourselves so instead we assume that others hold the same negative beliefs.

Pathogenic Beliefs: A set of beliefs that develop from traumatic experiences and influence the way in which we view and interact with the world.

Perfectionism: A compulsive striving for achievement, setting standards for oneself that are often unrealistic and contradictory. Perfectionism assumes that if we are just perfect enough, we can cancel out our bad feelings and rise above them, and all of our doubts and self-loathing will be assuaged.

Playing with Aggression: Attempting to enjoy a patient's aggression with them in a playful "as-if" kind of manner.

Pleasure Principle: Irrational, spontaneous thinking strategy employed by the id.

Positive Self-assertion: Healthy way of being able to assert oneself in appropriate situations

Process of Liberation: The process of working through the mask of the false self to the low self. Working through the low self leads to the love outraged of the core self. Working through the layers of the self in this way constitutes a path of transformation. The goal of the liberation process is to liberate the joyful, wise, and transcendent core self.

Projection: Usually thought of as placing feelings that we cannot accept in ourselves onto other people. For this text, projection consists of more: It is actually an unconscious assumption that everyone feels as we feel ourselves deep down, and we are unable accept this.

Prometheus' Chain: Chains that occur throughout life that bind us in promethean fashion, consisting of six important links: childhood hurt; the anger response to the hurt, which is the child's longing for love outraged; low self-esteem and unconscious guilt; gaining relief by bringing on our own punishments; denying negative feelings and destructive attitudes in ourselves and projecting them onto others, and compulsive dependency.

Psyche: The totality of the human mind, including the conscious and unconscious mind.

Psychic Injury: A mental harm, suffering, damage, impairment, or dysfunction that interferes with the way in which a person functions. These injuries cause pain that leads to a numbing of our core of love.

Psychic Pain: Anything that causes psychological pain or discomfort.

Psychological Subjectivity: Each person's needs, wishes, wants, dreams, ideas, and self-direction. The individual idiosyncratic elements of our personalities.

Psycho-spiritual Growth: Transformation of negative traits and faults we find in ourselves to positive life-affirming virtues.

Reality Principle: Rational, realistic thinking strategy from which the ego operates.

Recreation or Reenactment of Childhood Hurts: A reconstruction of our childhood difficulties in our later years—for example, choosing partners who resemble both the positive aspects of our parents as well as the way that they injured us.

Regression: A secondary defense mechanism in which a person reverts to an earlier stage of development in the face of thoughts or impulses that are unacceptable to the self-esteem or ego.

Relational or Intersubjective Technique: These theories place the therapist–client relationship at the forefront of therapeutic change. Both the therapist's and client's needs, foibles, and strengths are taken into consideration and are brought into the fray of reenactments of trouble spots within the relationship. Intersubjective therapy focuses on shared meaning and the here-and-now process that occurs between the therapist and the client.

Renunciation: The strong ego's avenue of coping in which negative impulses and feelings are recognized as human emotions but are not acted on; instead they are contained in our conscious awareness until they can be transformed back to their loving state.

Rigid Ego: When the ego has become too tight or over controlled, it defends against unconscious negativity with too much repression and other defense mechanisms.

"Rulership" Needs: See Ego Omnipotence

Seeking Punishment: A component of the Prometheus Chain, where we believe that since we are going to be punished, we decide to punish ourselves as a way to maintain some control and dignity.

Self-Confrontation: Examining our own behaviors and attitudes to make gainful changes. Finding and correcting the flaws in one's own personality and behaviors.

Self-Examination: Examining and reflecting on your own internal thoughts, feelings, memories, and action to learn from yourself and determine meaning.

Self-Object Needs: In infancy, children need an immediate felt sense that primary objects are empathically attuned and responsive.

Self-Reflection: Suspending judgments about how we are supposed to be in an effort to see ourselves as we truly are.

Self Will: The compulsion to have things go our way at all times regardless of consequences.

Spite: A desire to deliberately hurt, annoy, or punished someone, which is developed as a way to have the parent or other cared-for authorities bend to the will of the child.

Strong Ego: When the ego is able to contain feelings and examine them for their underlying meaning to eventually transform them into a more loving state. At this point, the ego has become strong and resilient and is able to accept unflattering desires, wishes, and experiences into awareness. This acceptance allows for mourning and transformation of the unwanted wishes and experiences.

Subjectivity-Embracing Position: When parents understand their child's dysphoria, complaints, and feelings, rather than punishing or rejecting the child for them. Helps the child to shape their own subjective wishes, wants, and desires in alliance with the child's organic readiness to grow and develop.

Sublimation: A defense or process that reorganizes more primitive conflictual impulses into more benevolent, acceptable ones.

Substituted Needs: When a person cannot fulfill a need, they may cope by substituting the unfilled need with its opposite.

Superego: The superego is the part of the mind in Freud's structural theory that acts as a self-critical conscience that is based on internalized rules and standards learned from our parents, teachers, and laws.

Superego "Over I": We introduce this term in the beginning but then do not use it again so I am not sure if it should be in the glossary.

Transference: The unconscious phenomenon of displacing and transferring feelings from one person to another; in therapy, feelings from previous and current relationships existing outside of the session are often transferred onto the therapist.

Transforming-duality process: A process that points to our deepest psychological fears and anxieties and aims at their transformation; a process of containing and accepting negative feelings in order to move beyond existential fear

Trauma: Especially potent in early life, this severe emotional or physical experience causes lasting physical, psychological, and/or emotional impairment.

Unconscious Guilt: An ego state resulting from a conflict between the "should have done" aims of the superego and the ego. An automatic sense of feeling bad about oneself and being undeserving of good things, leading to an unconscious bitter resentment.

Unhealthy Needs: Needs that are against love and therefore against the real self and others. Motivational impulses that are against or intend to do harm to our real self and others based on issues of vanity, power appearances, and egoism.

Unitive State of the World: The ultimate reality and truth that illuminates awareness of the interconnectedness with others and all life. Brings about a felt sense of empathy with others and a connectedness to our feelings that can resolve ethical dilemmas where outer rules fail us.

Weak Ego: When the ego is too weak, feelings threaten to override the control and balance in the personality. The weak ego contains real feelings that have deviated from their origin in love and have become negative and destructive due to trauma or the pains of life and our own ignorance.

Will: The impulse to self-direct, to affect our world and create ourselves.

About the Authors

Franklin Sollars PhD is a psychologist/psychoanalyst, professor of graduate studies, and the author of *Love Outraged and the Liberation of the Core Self*. He has also published many articles in psychoanalytic journals and is a writer and director for a soon-to-be-released film,

"Pirates of the North Coast." He is also Clinical Director of Sollars and Associates Integrative Counseling and Psychological Services across Michigan.

He has spent much of his life working with the intersection of psychoanalytic and mystical thought, which has brought him to the publication of his most recent book with co-author Jamie Sharpe—*The Love Outraged Workbook*. The Workbook provides exercises, examples, and meditations that help readers work with the concepts of trauma and healing of the human suffering that trauma causes. The Workbook also uses the injuries of our past as stepping stones to emotional and spiritual growth.

Michael Eigen, author of *Faith, The Psychotic Core,* and *The Birth Experience*, wrote about Sollars:

> Sollars writes profoundly about a deep core in the personality and paths leading towards and away from it. In this, he lines up with a great tradition of writing that affirms the depths of the human condition and attempts to delineate factors that enable sound development.

You can learn more about Franklin Sollars by searching Franklin Sollars PhD, or *Love Outraged* from University Professors Press, or potnc.wordpress.com.

Jamie Sharpe, MA (PsyD anticipated in 2020) is a limited licensed psychologist and graduate student pursuing her doctorate degree in clinical psychology. She is in the last year of her program and expects to graduate in 2020 after completing her internship and dissertation. Despite the innumerable hours Jamie has spent writing her dissertation, her love for writing has not wavered. Through her passion for psychology and the power of words, Jamie aspires to apply the art of writing in a way that

helps others heal and grow.

Also Available from University Professors Press

Love Outraged and the Liberation of the Core Self
by Franklin Sollars, PhD

Available at:
www.universityprofessorspress.com

Other Books by University Professors Press

The Polarized Mind: Why It's Killing Us and What We Can Do About It
by Kirk J. Schneider

The Spirituality of Awe: Challenges to the Robotic Revolution
by Kirk J. Schneider

Existential Psychology East–West (Volume 1, Revised & Expanded
Edition) by Louis Hoffman, Mark Yang, Francis J. Kaklauskas, Albert
Chan, & Monica Mansilla

Existential Psychology East–West (Volume 2)
by Louis Hoffman, Mark Yang, Monica Mansilla, Jason Dias, Michael
Moats, & Trent Claypool

Bare: Psychotherapy Stripped
by Jaqueline Simon Gunn with Carlo DeCarlo

Humanistic Contributions for Psychology 101
by Richard Bargdill and Rodger Broomé

Psychotherapy's Pilgrim-Poet: The Story Within
by Betsy Hall

*Shadows & Light: Theory, Research, & Practice in Transpersonal
Psychology* (Volumes 1 & 2)
by Francis J. Kaklauskas, Carla Clements, Dan Hocoy, & Louis Hoffman

*Reflections on Certain Qualitative and Phenomenological Psychological
Methods*
by Amedeo Giorgi

Psychology as a Human Science: A Phenomenologically Based Approach
by Amedeo Giorgi

Stanley Krippner: A Life of Dreams, Myths, and Visions
by Jeannine A. Davies & Daniel B. Pitchford

Single Sex Stories: Tales of Unmarried Sexuality and Faith
by Stephen W. Simpson

The Buddha, the Bike, the Couch, and the Circle: A Festschrift for Dr. Robert Unger
by Michael M. Dow, Francis J. Kaklauskas, & Elizabeth Olson

An Artist's Thought Book (2nd Edition)
by Richard Bargdill

Capturing Shadows: Poetic Encounters Along the Path of Grief & Loss
by Louis Hoffman & Michael Moats

Journey of the Wounded Soul: Poetic Companions for Spiritual Struggles
by Louis Hoffman & Steve Fehl

Our Last Walk: Using Poetry for Grieving and Remembering Our Pets
by Louis Hoffman, Michael Moats, & Tom Greening

Poems for and about Elders (Revised & Expanded Edition)
by Tom Greening

Stay Awhile: Poetic Narratives on Multiculturalism and Diversity
by Louis Hoffman & Nathaniel Granger, Jr.

Words Against the Void: Poems by an Existential Psychologist (Revised & Expanded Edition)
by Tom Greening

Connoisseurs of Suffering: Poetry for the Journey to Meaning
by Jason Dias & Louis Hoffman

Silent Screams: Poetic Journeys Through Addiction & Recovery
by Nathaniel Granger, Jr., & Louis Hoffman

A Walk with Nature: Poetic Encounters that Nourish the Soul
by Michael Moats, Derrick Sebree, Jr., Gina Subia Belton, & Louis Hoffman

CPSIA information can be obtained
at www.ICGtesting.com
Printed in the USA
LVHW080540241120
672556LV00006B/510

9 781939 686527